Reminiscence and Recall

A guide to good practice

care professional handbook series

Reminiscence and Recall

A guide to good practice

Faith Gibson

BOOKS

In memory of my friends Douglas, Florence and Jan
who proved beyond doubt that

'Everyone has a story to tell
If only someone will ask
If only someone will listen.' (Anon)

Bulk orders
Age Concern England is pleased to offer customised editions of all its titles to UK
companies, institutions or other organisations wishing to make a bulk purchase. For
further information, please contact the Publishing Department at the address above.
Tel: 0181-679 8000. Fax: 0181-679 6069. Email: addisom@ace.org.uk.

CONTENTS

About the Author   vii

Acknowledgements   viii

1   Introduction   1

2   What is Reminiscence Work?   10

3   Why Encourage Reminiscence Work?   20

4   How to Plan a Reminiscence Group   30

5   How to Run a Reminiscence Group   53

6   Reminiscence with Individuals   75

7   Reminiscence with Ethnic Minority Elders   92

8   Reminiscence with People with Dementia   105

9   Reminiscence with People who are Depressed   127

10 Reminiscence with People with Hearing, Sight and
    Speech Disabilities   137

11 Reminiscence with People with Learning Disabilities   145

12 How to Develop Reminiscence Work and Sustain
    Good Practice   152

References   158

Appendix 1
Recording Sheets   163

Appendix 2
Reminiscence and National Vocational Qualifications   174

Appendix 3
Resource Agencies   177

About Age Concern   184

Publications from Age Concern Books   185

Index   193

ABOUT THE AUTHOR

Faith Gibson, OBE, is an Emeritus Professor of Social Work, University of Ulster in Northern Ireland. She trained as a social worker and teacher in the Universities of Sydney, Queensland and Chicago, and has been a social work teacher, researcher and practitioner in child care and mental health agencies.

Her reminiscence publications include various trigger packages and training materials, and: 'What can reminiscence contribute to people with dementia?' in J Bornat (ed) *Reminiscence Reviewed: Evaluation, achievements and perspectives*; 'The use of the past' in A Chapman and M Marshall (eds) *Dementia: New skills for social workers*; and 'Owning the past in dementia care: creative engagement with others in the present' in M Marshall (ed) *State of the Art in Dementia Care*.

She writes about reminiscence and recall from wide practical experience of reminiscence work with individuals and small groups, including people with dementia. She firmly believes that skills can be learned and practice improved if reminiscence workers are willing to read, to examine their work critically, and to discuss it openly with other interested people.

ACKNOWLEDGEMENTS

In preparing this second edition I continue to be indebted to many people, both directly and indirectly, for their help and encouragement. Special thanks to Dorothy Atkinson, Michael Bender, Joanna Bornat, Jeremy Fennell, Pam Schweitzer and to all who have shared their rich recollections with me over many years, either as individuals or as members of small groups.

I have taken account of other people's research, practice experience and writings, and have drawn on ideas from many published sources. Sharing ideas with other reminiscence practitioners, researchers and theorists has been immensely valuable, but for the views expressed in this handbook, I take full responsibility.

I continue to be involved in different aspects of reminiscence training, practice and research in various countries. I value my close association with Age Exchange and the members of the European Reminiscence Network through which I experience, first hand, the power of reminiscence to transcend differences of age, gender, geography, ethnicity, nationality, language and professional background. Reminiscence builds bridges between people. Through reminiscence — the sharing of our life experience, with all its similarities and differences — we discover the riches in other people and recognise our common humanity.

Despite the growing international recognition reminiscence now attracts and its developing research base, its full potential to enrich, inform, entertain and heal still remains largely unexplored and underutilised by too many older people and those who live and work with them.

Reminiscence is both science and art. On-going research is essential. Knowledge and understanding grow and develop each time those engaged in reminiscence critically reflect on that experience and share their ideas with others.

This handbook is one small contribution to introducing people to good practice. It is written to help establish sensitive, responsive reminiscence work for the mutual benefit of older people, their families, friends, volunteers and professional carers.

Faith Gibson

July 1998

1 Introduction

This chapter includes:

- Suggestions about how to use this handbook
- The lifetime needs of people
- The multiple journeys people travel throughout their lives

This book is meant for people caring for an older person, especially those who would like to know more about the importance of reminiscence in later life and how to use knowledge about a person's past to enrich life in the present. The chapters that follow contain guidelines, suggestions rather than prescriptions, to help you develop good practice in reminiscence work with both individuals and small groups.

There is much more to be learned about reminiscence work than can be covered in this introductory guide, but careful further reading, attention to the application exercises and discussion of your work with others will help you get started.

Whether you do small groupwork or individual work in a residential care home, nursing home, hospital, club or day centre, or look after a person in their own home as a home care assistant, relative, friend or volunteer, this book should help you to develop high standards of reminiscence work.

It is important to remember two things about reminiscing. First, not all older people like to look back and to recall the past, so you must always be guided by the person's own wishes. If some people are not able to express their opinion clearly, you must still make sure that reminiscence is not forced on them. People are usually able to show by their behaviour, if not in words, whether or not they want to reminisce. Second, if you invite a person to tell you about their past, you must have time to listen. Reminiscence is not a process to be rushed.

This handbook will help you develop the attitudes, knowledge, understanding, values and skills needed to encourage people to value themselves by valuing their past. Whether you are a paid carer or a family carer, reminiscence can enrich your relationships and enhance your caring. This means that you, as well as older people, can benefit from reminiscence work.

Try to work through this book and its application exercises with a colleague or friend; discuss your ideas with each other. Try also to find an experienced reminiscence worker, supervisor or consultant who can help you understand the opportunities and demands which reminiscence work makes.

It is important to attempt to put into practice, as you go along, the things you will read about, because this is the way to develop skills. By trying out the ideas, you will experience first hand the infectious excitement of reminiscence work. Develop the habit of thinking back over the reminiscence work you have done so that, the next time you try, you will become more skilled. This is also a way of taking responsibility for your own learning.

Most people find it easier to do reminiscence work if they share it with at least one other trusted person so that together you can experience its ups and downs. You will be able to discuss what happens, support and constructively criticise each other, and through this mutual help make sure that good quality reminiscence work becomes firmly established.

If you are undertaking a National Vocational Qualification (NVQ) or Scottish Vocational Qualification (SVQ), it may be possible to use the application exercises and work reports (see Appendix 1, page 163) as part of a portfolio for assessment purposes. You will need to discuss this possibility with your workplace assessor, work supervisor and line manager to obtain their advice and agreement. Further information about relevant NVQs is given in Appendix 2 (page 174).

A good place to begin is to examine your ideas about older people. How do you regard older people?

You may look at old age in two different ways: you may see people either as growing old or as being old and still growing. Whichever view you hold will greatly influence how you treat older people and what you are prepared to do with them and for them. Everyone, of any age, is a unique individual. In some ways, people might resemble others in their age group but, in many more ways, each person is different. The longer people live, the more likely they are to differ from each other. So do not make the mistake of treating older people as if they were all the same. You like to be treated as a unique person. So do they.

Everyone, whatever their age, has common human needs, but the way that these needs have been met or denied will largely determine what people are like when they reach late life. Everyone is born with certain characteristics, called nature. Then, depending on what happens to them throughout life, known as nurture, they reach late life with some degree of resilience, acceptance, contentment and a sense of coherence or else they may feel demoralised, depressed, anxious, unhappy and unfulfilled.

A person is very seldom all one thing or the other. Most older people display a mixture of both positive and negative characteristics, depending on how nature and nurture have interacted throughout their life. Present circumstances, relationships and living arrangements also influence which characteristics and related behaviour predominate in the here and now.

While it is important to provide good physical care for older people, including comfortable, secure, warm accommodation, acceptable food, and medical care if required, more is needed. A strong sense of personal worth and identity, with a belief or feeling that essential aspects of life are still under one's own control, also influence how a person ages. In helping to provide love, security and a sense of belonging, carers and care environments can help people maintain their sense of worth, self-esteem and personal identity. In many ways, both large and small, older people can be helped to feel in control. This is very important if they are to experience a sense of fulfilment and well-being until the very end of their lives.

You may ask, 'How is it possible to meet all these needs and does it really matter if I do not?' Growing is a lifetime experience. People, whatever their age, can continue to grow and develop provided they experience the right nurturing conditions. You, but not only you, have a responsibility to help to meet older people's needs and so encourage their continued growth and development by:

- providing a warm, caring relationship;
- respecting each person as a unique individual;
- genuinely listening, attending and communicating in the present;
- learning about, understanding and accepting past life history;
- encouraging people to help each other;
- making certain that people have real choices;
- providing opportunities for interesting, stimulating activities so that people do not have to spend their time 'busy doing nothing'.

This book aims to help you become more competent in reaching out to older people in order to share their continuing journey towards growth, development and personal fulfilment. It is especially concerned with reminiscence and how you might encourage older people to use reminiscence in making sense of these long journeys which they have travelled to the present. It will help you to learn about the interesting, intriguing and complex lives they have lived. It will assist you to use the past to enrich the present.

There is much more to older people than just what you see in the present. No one, not even the apparently most ordinary person, reaches late life without a tremendous variety of good and bad, constructive and destructive, positive and negative, rewarding and unrewarding experiences behind them. Not only cats have nine lives!

Everyone has lived an intricate, interwoven series of lives. For example, as children, adolescents, students, lovers, partners, spouses, parents, workers, immigrants, grandparents, widows or widowers. If you are to begin to understand why someone is as they are now, in late life, you have to know something about what has gone before and what meaning the older person attaches to their life experiences. You need to learn to listen to their stories, to what they say, and to the spaces in between their words.

Reminiscence is a fruitful way of learning about such experience and its personal meaning. Through reminiscing, older people may be helped to review, rework and re-evaluate their lives. This process helps them to develop new perspectives, and perhaps to become more accepting of their life, however it has turned out.

Reminiscence may be very private but usually it is a two-way process in which people share recollections with each other. This mutual process then becomes an effective means of bridging the gap that so often exists between people of different ages, gender, social background, sexual orientation, class, race, religion, education, status, position and power.

Often it is hard for younger staff, family members and volunteers to find things in common with older people. Middle-aged carers are frequently preoccupied with concerns about their own parents, their own ageing or their own children. By becoming involved in reminiscence, experiences may be shared and relationships enriched.

Think of life as a tapestry. As well as looking at the 'wrong' side with all its tangles and untidiness that represent how people seem to be in the present – possibly bored, preoccupied, frustrated, complaining, frightened or overwhelmed – look at the 'other' side. Use reminiscence to discover the rich, complex, colourful, patterns of people's whole long lives. When this new view emerges, both you and they are enriched because you begin to share a journey together which will take you both in new, exciting and unexpected directions.

Perhaps you already know this poem which was found in the bedside locker of an elderly woman after her death in hospital. It illustrates how important it is to look beyond present outward appearances. It also shows how much this woman wanted her various journeys or pathways through life to be understood and appreciated.

A Crabbit Old Woman

What do you see nurse, what do you see?
What are you thinking when you're looking at me?
A crabbit old woman, not very wise,
Uncertain of habit with far away eyes,
Who dribbles her food and makes no reply,
When you say in a loud voice 'I do wish you'd try'.
Who seems not to notice the things that you do,
And is forever losing a stocking or shoe,
Who tries not to help you, try as you will,
With bathing and feeding, the long day to fill.
If that's what you're thinking, if that's what you see,
Then open your eyes nurse. You're not looking at me.

I'll tell you who I am as I sit so still,
As I rise at your bidding and eat at your will.
I'm a small child of ten with a father and mother,
And brothers and sisters, who love one another.
A young girl of sixteen with wings on her feet,
Dreaming that soon now, a true love she'll meet.
A bride soon at twenty, my heart gives a leap,
Remembering the vows that I promised to keep.
At twenty-five now I have young of my own,
Who need me to build a secure happy home.
A woman of thirty, my young growing fast,
Bound to each other with ties that should last.
At forty my young sons will soon all be gone,
But my man stays beside me to see I don't mourn.

At fifty, once more babies play round my knee,
Again we know children, my loved one and me.

Dark days are upon me, my husband is dead,
Look at the future, I shudder with dread,

For my young ones are busy, making homes of their own,
And I think of the years and the love that I've known.
I'm an old woman now, nature is cruel,
It's her jest to make old age look like a fool.
The body, it crumbles, grace and vigour depart,
There now is a stone where I once had a heart.
But inside this old carcass, a young girl still dwells,
And now and again my battered heart swells.
I remember the joys, I remember the pain,
And I'm loving and living life over again.
And I think of the years, all too few, gone too fast,
And accept the stark fact that nothing can last.
So open your eyes nurse, open and see,
Not a crabbit old woman, look closer, see me.

Another poem, also by an anonymous writer, captures the important idea that age is socially constructed – it is not determined by years alone but depends, to some extent at least, on the inter-play between how old people see themselves, how others see them, and the continuing opportunities they have to remain involved in life.

Age

Age is a quality of mind
If you have left your dreams behind
If hope is cold
If you no longer plan ahead
If your ambitions all are dead
Then you are old.
But if you make of life the best
And in your life you still have zest
If love you hold
No matter how the birthdays fly
You are not old.

KEY POINT

■ To do effective reminiscence work you need to have a real interest in who people are and how they have lived their lives.

APPLICATION EXERCISE

Try to imagine yourself when old and consider how the following might contribute to you having a sense of fulfilment and well-being in the present. If you find this too difficult, think about a specific older person you know. Try to put yourself in his or her shoes and then ask yourself:

■ Is this person in good physical and mental health?

■ Do they feel financially secure?

■ Have they experienced a major change, threat, loss or bereavement, particularly in the last few years?

■ Do they have regular contact with a close friend, companion or confidant?

■ Are satisfying stimulation, occupation, interests and activities available?

■ How well are care needs being met?

■ Do they feel in control of their life and present circumstances?

Further Reading

Wholeness in Later Life by R Bright. Jessica Kingsley, London, 1997.

Ageing in Society: An introduction to social gerontology by S Bond, P Coleman and S Peace (eds). Sage, London, 1993.

Remembering Our Past: Studies in autobiographical memory by D C Rubin (ed). Cambridge University Press, Cambridge, 1996.

Dementia Reconsidered by T Kitwood. Buckingham, Open University, 1997.

2 What is Reminiscence Work?

This chapter includes:

- Two definitions of reminiscence
- A very brief history of reminiscence work
- Reminiscence as reminiscence work, not reminiscence therapy
- Who should undertake reminiscence work?

APPLICATION EXERCISE

What do you think reminiscence is?

Before reading further, write down your own ideas.
Then compare them with what others have said, as quoted in
this chapter. Start with your own ideas first.

Two definitions of reminiscence

Reminiscence is defined by people in different ways, but two wide-ly accepted definitions are:

'Reminiscence is the act or process of recalling the past.' (Butler 1963)

and

'The process or practice of thinking or talking about past experience.'
(Romaniuk & Romaniuk 1981)

Reminiscence may refer to either a single memory or a whole series of connected memories, which may remain private thoughts or be shared in various forms, most commonly as spoken recollections.

A brief history of reminiscence work

Throughout history and in most cultures there have always been special storytellers as well as ordinary people who enjoyed passing on their experience to others by recalling the past. Some of these people wrote down their recollections while others relied on word of mouth. This oral passing on of traditions used to be called folklore or, more recently, oral history. Although such activities were accepted by some, many professional carers believed that the tendency for people to reminisce more as they grew older, to 'live in the past', was a negative side of growing older. It was to be deplored, not valued, to be discouraged, not encouraged.

It is only in the last 35–40 years that health and social care professionals have begun to realise the importance to older people of being able to look back, to recall the past and to share their recollections with others. Reminiscence, an ordinary everyday activity, has come to be valued and to be used for educational, recreational, social and therapeutic purposes.

Increasingly, writers have emphasised the importance of understanding why some older people feel compelled to talk about the past and how important it is to treat each person as a unique individual. In the mid-seventies, Kemp (1978), an architect by training, when working for the Department of Health and Social Security in London studied residential institutions for older people. He realised that '... unlike old people at large, nobody was talking about their past. There was a very real belief amongst caring professionals that it was wrong to encourage reminiscence as it interfered with a proper grip on today's reality.'

He persuaded Gordon Langley, a psychiatrist, and a small team of artists and psychologists to help him to develop a reminiscence aid. Kemp's pioneering work was carried forward by Help the Aged, who, in 1981, published the three-part tape/slide package *Recall*. This aid encouraged the dramatic growth and extensive development of reminiscence because it provided busy staff in residential homes, hospitals and day centres with an accessible working tool. Occupational therapists and activity nurses also recognised the potential for social stimulation that reminiscence provided. Many other more local aids similar to *Recall* have since been produced and many carers now use reminiscence in countless ways in their day-to-day caring work.

A number of American clinicians and researchers were already writing about the many different facets and functions of reminiscence. Their work provided the early theoretical underpinning for the British work which blossomed with the publication of *Recall*. In the years since, interest has spread to many other countries. Training, education, drama and publishing work promoted by Age Exchange Reminiscence Centre in Blackheath, London has become the focus for the development of the European Reminiscence Network. The Network, which is supported by EU funding, engages in transnational research and development projects; inter-generational and international theatre performances; publications, including *Reminiscence*, the Network's journal; and international conferences which provide a fruitful meeting place for creative artists, health and social care professionals, older people and volunteers.

The increasing popularity of reminiscence has also coincided with a growing interest in oral history and local history. Historians are interested in making an accurate record of the past; they are less interested in the processes of remembering but have become increasingly aware of the effect on interviewer and informant of the interview experience. They use focused oral evidence in seeking to understand and interpret history. For them, the outcome, product or account, is central. Because many reminiscence groups, although primarily interested in providing personal fulfilment, communication and social stimulation, are also interested in producing a record of shared collective memories, it is not always easy to distinguish precisely between some reminiscence work and oral history.

In oral history and folklore there are traditions of collecting and recording memories, both with individuals and in groups, but the emphasis until recently has been more on recording individuals. Most reminiscence has been undertaken in small groups but individual work, often called 'life history' or 'life story' work is also growing in popularity. As Joanna Bornat (1989) has suggested, reminiscence work, like oral history can be thought of as a democratisation process – of giving people their place. In the health and social care services, reminiscence groupwork and individual life story work are now undertaken in many hospitals, nursing and residential homes and day centres.

With increasing numbers of frail older people continuing to live at home, domiciliary carers also need to understand about the importance of reminiscence. They will have many spontaneous opportunities to reminisce in their ordinary conversation with older people or while undertaking other care tasks. Sometimes they may also want to use planned reminiscence as part of a package of care to enrich communication. Family carers also can benefit by learning to use reminiscence but it is not always easy for them to find the time and energy required. More might be encouraged to do so if they were assisted by trained volunteers. The increasing numbers of frail older people living alone could also benefit from regular visits by reminiscence volunteers.

Recognising the importance of the past has liberated both older people and their professional carers. People are now free to remember. You as a carer are free to encourage them and to share in remembering. As Dobrof (1984) said: 'In a profound sense, Butler's writings liberated both the old and the nurses, doctors and social workers; the old were free to remember, to regret, to look back reflectively at the past and try to understand it. And we were free to listen and to treat rememberers and remembrances with the respect they deserved.'

Characteristics of reminiscence

Different kinds of reminiscence can be distinguished. It may be a private or a public process. It may be undertaken with an individual on their own, by a worker with one other person, or it may be a much more public process in which memories are shared with other people in a small group with each person contributing their recollections.

Reminiscence is usually cumulative, which means that one memory leads on to another. One person's shared recollections usually spark off associated recollections in others. This in turn stimulates further memories which lead to further modification or expansion of the stories being recounted.

Both private and public reminiscence may be spontaneous, unintended, or memories and talk about memories may be purposely and deliberately encouraged. Whether recall is spontaneous or prompted may influence the memories recalled, whether they relate to the distant or the recent past, to recollection of knowledge or to autobiographical life experience. This handbook is primarily concerned with encouraging good practice in prompted or planned recall about personal life experience but also seeks to widen understanding about the value of spontaneous recall.

Reminiscence may be internal, something that goes on inside a person, or it may be externalised. By translating images into speech, writing, poetry, drawing, painting, drama, mime, music, dance or some other communication medium, the recollections have the potential to be shared with others. This process of sharing enriches the experience for both teller and listener, providing the storyteller experiences the listener as genuinely interested, and totally without patronising condescension.

In the telling and retelling, the detail of a memory alters somewhat. Both the context and interaction between the teller and the listener influences the story. It does not matter if the details change. Think of it more as a picture being painted and repainted in changing light. While the major characteristics or core remain recognisable, the details alter, reflecting differences of emphasis, mood, memory and interpretation. Our recollections will always be coloured by such personal interpretation because, as Pear (1922) suggested, 'The mind never photographs. It paints pictures.'

Most people enjoy reminiscence, but remember that it does not suit everyone and it must never be hurried. You must never push people into reminiscence against their better judgement. Always respect their wishes. People of all ages reminisce, not just old people. There is a widely held belief that older people reminisce more than younger people. This is probably not true for spontaneous recall if older people are living active independent lives. Recalling memories about the distant, rather than the recent past probably increases in older people whose present lives are bleak or boring or where memories are being purposely prompted in reminiscence work by the use of aids or triggers.

Not all reminiscence can be about happy memories because no person's life consists only of 'good old days'. Reminiscence recalls past pain as well as past happiness, past loss as well as past joys. Reminiscence is not about sentimental, nostalgic 'trips down memory lane'. If you want to do reminiscence work, you must be prepared for, and able to cope with, whatever kinds of recollections and their associated emotions may emerge. More guidance about this is given in Chapter 9, 'Reminiscence with People who are Depressed'.

This book does not talk about 'reminiscence therapy' although many writers do. Instead, the term 'reminiscence work' is preferred. This is because reminiscence is viewed as a mutual process, a shared journey. Older people are not ill and awaiting treatment by expert reminiscence professionals, as the word 'therapy' implies. Rather, they are the teachers, informants, authorities and stores of invaluable information about the past.

Your task generally as a reminiscence worker is to help older people to share their life-long experience with you and with others, now in the present. While talking about the past, people are communicating in the present. In the process you too will be enriched. Older people, care staff, volunteers and family members can benefit from using this ordinary everyday process. In this sense, reminiscence is therapeutic even though it is not strictly a therapy.

Reminiscence work includes many different approaches depending on the level of knowledge, skill, confidence and experience of the people who use it. It is not a set of precisely defined and rigorously tested techniques. Instead, it is a loose collection of ideas resulting in varied approaches, activities and practices that differ according to the specific objectives of the work, who does it and where it takes place.

Small reminiscence groupwork and individual life history work described in this handbook both differ from recreational and social activities such as trips to museums, tea dances, fashion shows, old-time musical functions, film or slide shows, which usually involve much larger numbers of people. Within such activities, however, there will be many opportunities for spontaneous reminiscence, or these large events may be used as a springboard for more intimate reminiscence work at a later time.

In hospitals, nursing homes and residential homes, where people live in groups, reminiscence is usually undertaken as a small group activity. Some people, however, are much more suited to individual work and it is a mistake to assume that because people live in groups they should only be involved in groupwork.

It is helpful to distinguish between *general* and *specific* reminiscence work.

General work refers to well planned work that uses open-ended questions or various triggers to stimulate recall on topics likely to interest the participants. General work usually employs easily available materials, or triggers, to encourage recall of readily accessible memories. It is likely to emphasise sociability, educational and recreational objectives. It is more likely, but not always, to be undertaken in a group.

An example is a group of eight women in a residential home who meet with two staff members for weekly sessions to look at library books, photographs and newspaper cuttings about women's work and to share with each other their memories about their own working lives.

Specific reminiscence is more likely, but not invariably, to be undertaken with individuals or in small formed groups. It refers to carefully selected, focused, precise use of special triggers designed to be of immediate relevance to the people concerned. It is likely to use materials either owned by or closely associated with the participants and is particularly relevant to work with individuals who may have dementia or are depressed, demoralised or disturbed. The objectives of the work are likely to be to increase self-acceptance, to enhance self-esteem, confirm personal identity, or possibly to achieve behavioural change. A structured life review with an individual or guided autobiographical writing in a group would be types of specific work.

An example is a man with early dementia attending a day centre. He is unhappy, aggressive towards others and isolated. A worker spends time twice-weekly with him to talk about his earlier family life, work and retirement. Together they write a life history and match his story with photographs obtained from his family.

Depending on people's differing circumstances and needs, either general or specific work may be more appropriate. Each approach requires skilled workers prepared to undertake careful planning, preparation and review. Both approaches can considerably improve people's quality of life by enhancing communication. Before starting, it is important to decide what kind of reminiscence work may be more appropriate where you work and what best suits the needs and interests of the people in your care.

Who should undertake reminiscence work?

This is an important question because some professionals may wish to claim reminiscence as their exclusive territory. Reminiscence is not the monopoly of any one profession. It is not necessarily the monopoly of any profession. Many different people employed in health and social care work, including residential care, day care, nursing, social work, librarianship, clinical psychology, occupational therapy, speech therapy, diversional and activity therapy do reminiscence work. So, too, do volunteers or others with few recognised qualifications. Inter-generational work usually involves teachers or youth workers. Family carers too are increasingly being encouraged to appreciate and to use the rich possibilities of reminiscence.

Attitudes, values, knowledge and skills are more important than any particular professional background. Skills can be learned, and those needed for effective reminiscence work include:

- active listening – 'listening with the third ear';
- empathising – sharing another's world without losing hold of your own;
- attending – being available to people;
- relating sensitively – not being a bull in a china shop;
- being able to respect and to value people as unique individuals;
- not being frightened by the expression of painful emotions;
- being able to enjoy reminiscence and be interested in the past;
- being disciplined, but willing to share your own reminiscences;
- being able to reflect upon and to criticise your own work;
- being able to accept and offer criticism.

KEY POINTS

- Reminiscence and recall indicate mental health, not mental ill health.
- Some aspects of reminiscence resemble oral history.
- Reminiscence is more concerned with inter-personal processes than with achieving factually accurate history or tangible products.
- Not everyone wants to reminisce. Personal choice must be respected.
- Reminiscence may be undertaken with individuals, pairs or small groups.
- Memories have many facets, which may alter in the telling.
- Some memories may be very painful.
- Reminiscence is a process that must not be rushed.
- Reminiscence skills need to be learned through training, practice, reading and reflection.

APPLICATION EXERCISE

Ask yourself the following questions. Write down your answers. Try to find someone with whom you feel comfortable so that you can discuss your answers with them.

■ What aspects of reminiscence work appeal to me?

■ What aspects of reminiscence work worry me?

Further Reading

Reminiscence Reviewed: Evaluation, achievements and perspectives by J Bornat (ed). Open University, Buckingham, 1994.

The Art and Science of Reminiscence: Theory, research, methods and applications by B K Haight and J D Webster (eds). Taylor and Francis, London, 1995.

3 Why Encourage Reminiscence Work?

This chapter includes:

■ Ten reasons for doing reminiscence work with individuals and small groups
■ Other classifications of the functions of reminiscence

APPLICATION EXERCISE

Why do you think reminiscence might be important? Begin by writing down as many reasons as you can. If possible, get a colleague to do the same and then discuss your reasons with each other.

Ten reasons for doing reminiscence work

1 Reminiscence makes connections between a person's past, present and future

Our remembered past sheds light on the present and prepares us for facing an unknown future. It helps with problem solving. By looking back we are able to draw on evidence of past coping; we are encouraged in times present; and dare to hope we shall cope in the future.

Most people find moving into care, or sheltered housing, beginning to attend a day centre, or facing up to any new experience involving changed circumstances and meeting strangers, a daunting experience. Remember how you feel when you are 'new'. Put yourself in the shoes of older people who may have lost good health, independence, their own home, significant people, familiar places and possessions, and the routines of a lifetime. Reminiscence can help ease the anxiety of such major changes. If you can assist newcomers to draw on their past experience of coping they may be greatly encouraged in facing up to the inevitable demands of present and future changes.

2 Reminiscence encourages sociability and opens up new relationships

At a stage in people's lives when their social networks, meaning the significant people to whom each is connected, are probably shrinking because of death or changes in living arrangements, reminiscence may open up new relationships. It may help people to make new friends, or re-discover old friends, because it may help them see that other people have had similar experiences. They discover common ground. Talking about the past becomes a rich means of sharing experience in the present, of discovering new resources in each other.

Even if people live surrounded by others, in homes or hospitals, you must not assume that this means they have close, warm relationships. Some will; others may feel isolated, lonely and unhappy. They may be grieving for lost places, lost people and lost independence. They may be struggling with coming to terms with how to lead private lives in public places. The challenge for staff is how to help residents reconcile their need for personal privacy with their need for significant relationships. Both needs must be respected.

Joining a small reminiscence group may help solve this dilemma. Here the person can share those aspects of their lives that they choose to talk about. They remain in control of what they say about themselves but the leader enables them to talk in their own way and in their own time. As they begin to trust the other group members they will feel more confident about moving from superficial discussion to talking about experiences that are important to them. In sharing both pain and pleasure, each person learns to accept the others and new relationships emerge.

This process of growing towards others through sharing deeply felt emotions is not limited to groups. It also applies to reminiscence work with individuals. The possibilities, however, are enlarged and multiplied through group experience. Here each member has the potential for becoming a resource to every other member while at the same time benefiting themselves. The richness lies in both giving and receiving.

Care assistant 'We use reminiscence groups as a means of introducing a new member and to help them feel at home with us. Reminiscence helps them find other people from the same neighbourhood with similar backgrounds to whom they can talk in familiar ways. It gets them over the strangeness.'

3 Reminiscence confirms a sense of unique identity and encourages feelings of self-worth

A strong feeling of personal identity, of knowing who you are, gradually emerges in adolescence and young adulthood. This sense of identity is important at every age. It helps us to remain in control of our own lives and not to be overcome by the pressures that allow us to be treated as if we were either inhuman objects or just the same as everyone else.

As people grow older, some feel they are no longer valued by others, and some find it difficult to value themselves. All too easily they accept the negative ideas around them, diminishing their own significance, allowing themselves to be marginalised. By showing a genuine interest in the lives people have lived in the past, through reminiscence, you may be able to help rekindle or reinforce a sense of uniqueness, of personal identity and self-worth. In this way you will encourage people to value themselves in the present and to remain more in control of their own destiny.

4 Reminiscence assists the process of life review

The term 'life review' is used loosely as a general term and also in a more technical way. In general, many people as they grow older become increasingly aware of past experiences, especially painful, difficult, unfinished business or unresolved conflicts. Everyone has particular tasks to work on at different stages in their lives. The task or challenge that faces older people is to come to terms with life as it has turned out – for good or ill. Some become increasingly aware of trying to review, resolve, reorganise, reintegrate and tidy up their past experience in the face of encroaching age and approaching death. Dealing with the past becomes a preparation for death.

It does seem that for many, but not all, older people, if they can be helped to take a second look at their past, to 'put their house in order', they develop a kindlier view of themselves. You can help them in this process of life review by affirming that their life has been significant. In becoming easier on themselves, many become easier on others around them. Dealing with the past makes life in the present more bearable.

5 Reminiscence changes the nature of relationships

Reminiscence can be a most effective tool for improving communication and empathic understanding. By telling their story, people reach out to others at the same time that they are reaching deep down into themselves. A life story creates, sustains and alters relationships.

In almost all institutions (and in families too) there is a pecking order. Everybody, staff member, family member and resident alike, has their 'place'. Staff are always more powerful than residents. People with dementia are especially likely to experience a loss of significance or importance both within their own families and in institutions. However, reminiscence work in which residents, family members, volunteers and paid carers share experiences will help restore a sense of significance. In this sense reminiscence work can be 'empowering' for older people.

In understanding a person's past, it is easier to understand their present behaviour – even troubling and troubled behaviour. People become more finely tuned to each other's needs, more accepting of them and more able to reach out to each other. By reminiscing together, people learn to trust each other more as people and become less preoccupied with position, power and protocol. Because, in this sense, reminiscence is far-reaching, radical and unsettling, not everyone welcomes it.

6 Reminiscence alters others' perceptions and understanding

When you have only recently met someone, it is nearly impossible to understand why they are as they are now. Everyone travels many journeys to reach the present and some of these journeys are harder than others. Past experience leaves its mark. If, by listening to people reminisce, you come to learn about these different journeys, you will better understand the traveller in the present. Because you see the older person differently, you will treat them differently. The person is seen and appreciated as a unique individual. Your understanding is increased; your sympathies enlarged. You can help celebrate and value the heroism of remembered lives. If, on the other hand, the reminiscence reveals suffering caused to others in the past, you will need to distinguish between accepting the person but not accepting their past behaviour.

> **Matron of a residential home** 'I never understood why Hugh was so difficult, why he hated being here so much, until I heard him talk about his childhood. Now I see him differently, I understand him more and we have something to talk to each other about.'

7 Reminiscence aids assessment of present functioning and informs care plans

If you consider only how a person is in the present, it is like taking a single snapshot instead of looking through a whole photograph album. It is not a fair way to assess a person's present capacities. You cannot understand them now without knowing what they used to be like, what they used to be able to do, and liked to do. Their history suggests what they may still be able to do and what might still interest them, given half a chance. Reminiscence helps fill out the detail of a person's life history and helps illuminate the present. It is vital that assessments and care plans are based on all relevant information, both past and present, because judgements made by professionals can have profound consequences for influencing ill-being or wellbeing of people needing health and social care services.

In some care homes, reminiscence with a key worker may be an established way of assisting assessment, helping newcomers settle and developing a care plan. Life stories reveal how different people think about their own lives. The process of gathering a life story helps the carer to grasp the essence of the other person and understand how they view their present changed circumstances in the light of their life experience.

8 Reminiscence reverses the gift relationship

Those who have lived history are its best teachers. Bearing witness is important to many people as they grow older, and reminiscence may be described as seeing and seeing again, of telling and telling again.

Older people are tremendous sources of historical knowledge and, given encouragement, may be prepared to share it with younger people. Instead of being passive recipients of others' caring, of having things done for them and to them, through reminiscence they are able to move to the centre of the stage. As soon as older people become the teachers, their carers become the learners. In letting an older person become the authority, you become the student. They become the giver while you become the receiver. So reminiscence connects the storyteller to their own earlier life, to their contemporaries and to other generations.

9 *Reminiscence preserves and transmits the cultural heritage*

An unknown writer has suggested that each time an old person dies, history dies with them. A book is lost. This loss is felt most acutely by close family members. Encouraging families to discover and preserve their family history before it is too late can lead to great mutual excitement and shared pleasure between the generations in the present.

> **Family carer** 'Why did I leave it so late? I always meant to get Mum to tell me about the family but I never got around to it. When I was younger I was bored by her stories. When I was older I was too busy to bother. Now she's gone and we've lost her and we've lost the family history too.'

How much more positive is this daughter's recollection? 'For the last two years I have been doing mother's family tree. This has been a great interest for her as she was a great storyteller and had, right up to her death, an excellent memory. Reminiscence for her was a trip from P— where she grew up right through Ireland to all the towns she had lived in. They moved every five years because of my father's job so she had a lot to tell.'

If we learn to listen to people remembering and remember ourselves, we capture the past. If we tell someone else, record or write down the recollections, we help to preserve the past and transmit the culture. This applies as much to 'domestic' history as to national history. One is the record of so-called ordinary people telling about their ordinary lives. The other concerns national events which people may have witnessed, or the times they lived through when such events occurred. Bornat (1989), trained as an oral historian, writes about reminiscence as a social movement because reminiscence gives a voice to those not usually thought of as opinion formers. It provides raw material for oral history which Paul Thompson (1988) persuasively argues has become a respected part of historical studies.

10 Most people 'enjoy' reminiscence

This does not mean that all reminiscence is happy. Some recollections will be happy, others sad. Not everyone wants to reminisce. Respect any reticence or reluctance. Some people can only keep the painful past in its place by ignoring it. Others may be so taken up with living in the present and thinking about the future that they have no time or desire to think about the past. Most of us, however, get enormous satisfaction from recalling the past and sharing the personal meanings which we attach to our experience with empathetic, appreciative listeners. For many people and their carers reminiscence, especially in groups, gives intense pleasure, excitement and enjoyment. For others it is a diversion, a means of reducing boredom, of passing the time. For most it is a constructive occupation which may lead on to many other related activities.

Other classifications of reminiscence

Dorothy Langley, a drama therapist, and Gordon Langley (1983) asked, 'Why reminisce?' and then divided up this big question into five smaller questions:

- Is it to indulge a well-remembered past that competes unfavourably with less flattering and ill-related recent memories?
- Is it an attempt by a person nearing the end of life to leave a verbal or written memorial?
- Is it an updating of values and lifestyle, a levelling process, in which the present is met by drawing on a lifetime of experiences?
- Is it a social event in which ideas and images are shared and valued, identities established and communication initiated?
- Is it the process of recording history, distinguished or humble, written or oral, and therefore of perpetuating the culture of the storyteller?

They suggested that reminiscence may be any of these and, at its best, is probably all of them.

Webster (1997), a psychologist, has developed a Reminiscence Functions Scale (RFS) from which he derived eight factors representing the functions of reminiscence:

- boredom reduction
- identity
- conversation
- bitterness revival

- death preparation
- problem solving
- intimacy maintenance
- teaching/informing

Watt and Wong (1990) identified six reminiscence categories described as integrative, instrumental, transmissive, narrative, escapist and obsessive. People have different styles of reminiscing. As they tell their life story, the careful listener comes to understand whether the teller uses reminiscence in an *affirming*, a *negative* or a *despairing* way, as suggested by Fry (1994).

A person with an affirming style accepts both positive and negative life experiences. They are able to face conflicts or problems in their life and to have some hope that the difficulties can be resolved. They have a sense of wholeness about their life.

A person with a negative style of reminiscing presents life as gentle and pleasant. They ignore or play down painful experience, and often refer to public rather than personal experience as a means of distancing themselves from the impact of talking about their past. They play it safe.

A despairing style means that the person is painfully aware of, and probably preoccupied with, conflicts and negative experiences. These feelings emerge as a lack of fulfilment, pain and disappointment that they seem to be unable to repress, deny or grow beyond.

James McConkey (1997), a writer, sums up the importance of being able to remember: 'Memory is responsible for our identity: it is the faculty whereby we perceive connections between past and present, thus enabling us to make sense of our surroundings; it underlies our creative achievements.'

So you can see that although reminiscence is a very common everyday experience, it is not as simple as it first seems.

KEY POINTS

- The functions served by reminiscence will differ from person to person and for each person over time.
- Not all the identified functions apply to everyone.
- Try to understand what reminiscence means to you and to each individual at the life stage you and they have reached.
- Identify different styles of reminiscing
- Develop curiosity about your own and other people's past. Do not just see yourself and them through 'present spectacles'.

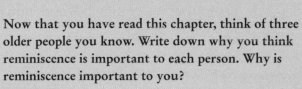

APPLICATION EXERCISE

Now that you have read this chapter, think of three older people you know. Write down why you think reminiscence is important to each person. Why is reminiscence important to you?

Discuss your answers with a colleague.

Further Reading

The Purpose of Reminiscence by M Bender, P Baukham and A Norris. Sage, London, 1998.

The Meaning of Reminiscence and Life Review by J Hendricks (ed). Baywood, Amityville, 1995.

4 How to Plan a Reminiscence Group

This chapter includes:

- Ideas about groupwork
- The responsibilities of senior staff
- The responsibilities of group leaders
- The preparation and planning phase of a group with guidelines

Much of the information about preparation for general groupwork in this chapter is also relevant to specific groupwork and individual work.

Ideas about groupwork

There are many different kinds of groups, models of groupwork and styles of leadership. Distinctions are not always as clear cut as the models suggest. One appropriate model for reminiscence work is a 'mutual aid' or 'reciprocal' group. This means a group where members are encouraged to join in shared discussion as equals on freely agreed topics. The leader acts as an enabler or facilitator, not an authority. He or she is responsible for creating a safe place within known boundaries and for encouraging members to talk with each other. The shared discussion about life experience within a warm supportive group, the group process, is the important aspect. The programme is used as a way of achieving this communication.

Some reminiscence groups are better described as activity groups. Here the emphasis is on 'doing'. The programme is important in itself, not just as a means to an end. Such groups concentrate on achieving an agreed outcome or a specific product. They are some-times known as task-centred groups.

Many local history groups which work towards recording, writing and publishing people's memories fit this category. Task groups may wish to achieve a specific outcome, such as preserving recollections by sound or video recording, writing or publishing. Some may wish to become historical informants or resources to other people such as school children or history students. Some groups will want to achieve a single event such as an exhibition, a reading of their writ-ten work, a play or performance based on members' recollections to which others are invited. Some may wish to establish a database or an archive. Reminiscence becomes part of the means for achieving these possible outcomes.

A group may have a main emphasis, but seldom are other aspects excluded. Many reminiscence groups in care settings begin as mutual aid or 'talk' groups but, during the lifetime of the group, members may decide to write down, publish, illustrate or exhibit the out-comes of their discussions. In such groups both the process and the product are important. In other groups which set out to be task cen-tred, members frequently gain other intangible benefits such as warmth, acceptance, friendship and improved self-esteem as their life experience comes to be valued by others.

Reminiscence, once begun, develops a dynamic of its own. If a show, book, exhibition or other products are produced, these in turn will stimulate further reminiscence by the audience, reader or viewer, so the process is continued.

Groups led by trained psychotherapists are called psychotherapeu-tic groups. These groups aim to help members get in touch with complex, painful, perhaps long-buried, memories and unresolved conflicts which 'leak' into the present and interfere with present contentment and adjustment. Recall of the past will play a large part in psychotherapeutic groups and in individual counselling and psychotherapy. This book does not attempt to prepare people for such highly skilled work, which requires professional training and close supervision.

Whatever the type of group, if it is a positive, nurturing, constructive experience it will indeed be 'therapeutic' in a general sense.

The responsibilities of senior staff

If you are a manager in a hospital ward, residential care or nursing home or day centre you are in a key position to ensure that the needs of the older people in your care for acceptance, warmth, respect, social and intellectual stimulation, companionship, and fulfilling activities are sensitively met.

You are responsible for creating a climate in which people feel valued and their life experience validated. You set the lead and other staff will follow. Reminiscence work will happen, and be done well, or will not happen, or be done badly, depending on the lead you give, the commitment you make and the resources you make available.

Find other staff who share your concerns, so that together you can create an active participative environment where each person is recognised as a unique individual with a long and interesting life history. Reminiscence work will flourish only if managers affirm its importance, staff are allowed time in which to do it (including time for preparation, de-briefing, and supervision) and feel their work is valued.

Continuity is important for successful individual work and group-work. So you must make sure that, if staff are committed to an agreed number of reminiscence sessions, then their duty rotas and workloads enable them to be available at the required times. As far as possible, you also need to ensure that participants are free from competing or conflicting demands which may make it hard for them to attend.

Some staff of all grades may not be convinced about the importance of reminiscence work. They may be sceptical about its value and critical of colleagues for wanting to spend time on something they regard as a 'soft option'. (This important point is further developed on pages 116–117 in relation to older people with dementia.) Do not let reminiscence work be undermined by such attitudes. Staff will quickly take their lead from managers.

All staff who wish to have an opportunity to develop their reminiscence skills should be encouraged to do so. Everyone can help in one way or another. All can be involved in locating materials, lending objects, making suggestions, and sharing in celebrating outcomes.

If you are introducing reminiscence work for the first time, it is helpful to discuss it at a staff meeting. Explain to the whole staff the basic ideas underlying reminiscence work. Tell them how you hope the group members and others may benefit and openly discuss ways in which all staff can contribute. Either take responsibility for supervising the reminiscence work yourself or for making alternative arrangements.

Practical details and issues of confidentiality will also require detailed discussion with the staff group. You need to agree what information arising from the reminiscence work will be shared, with whom and in what format. Who will have access to it? For example, what will be included in care plans? Who will be responsible for writing these and who will be entitled to read them? Will participants be involved in this process?

The responsibilities of group leaders

The different reasons for encouraging reminiscence were summarised in Chapter 3. Thinking about the people you are planning to work with, you may wish to concentrate on only some of these aspects and turn them into statements of objectives or outcomes. Before deciding who you wish to work with and for what purpose, you may want to consider issues concerning reminiscence with people with disabilities, some of which are covered in Chapters 8, 9, 10 and 11. Be realistic about what you want to achieve, and remember it is unwise to think that everything referred to can be accomplished for all group members in every group.

Writers on groupwork suggest that there are different phases or stages in the overall life of a group, from beginning to end. It is widely agreed that each group, throughout its life, as well as each separate meeting, moves through these stages. It is important to understand this because both leaders and members behave differently depending on which stage the group is at, both overall and within each session.

Shulman suggested:
- preliminary, preparation and planning
- beginnings
- middles
- endings

Tuckman suggested:
- forming
- storming
- norming
- performing

Tuckman describes 'forming' as the stage of getting together, becoming acquainted, making trial and error suggestions, and much indecision. 'Storming' is the stage when rules and boundaries are tested, anger is expressed and conflict recognised. The group then emerges into the 'norming' stage where agreement is reached about how members will work together, and finally 'performing' sees tasks accomplished.

This handbook uses Shulman's classification. The success of any small group, including a reminiscence group, largely depends on how carefully the leader(s) plans and prepares for it. Although careful preparation for each session is important, the first and last sessions are the most important. The beginning and ending phases within each separate session are also important because these are times of heightened emotions and hence important opportunities for work.

Preparation and planning phase of a group with guidelines

Before starting any new reminiscence group, consider the questions listed below. It is not possible to give standard answers to these questions but only general guidelines. Your own preparations will depend upon the objectives agreed for your group, the characteristics of its members and the context in which it is taking place.

You may think the list is far too detailed, but it is designed especially for workers who are new to reminiscence groupwork.

Setting possible outcomes

What do I hope this group will achieve for the members and for myself?

How am I going to explain this group to potential members?

GUIDANCE

You can either set objectives which look forward in anticipation to what you hope will be achieved or outcomes which look back to what you hope will have been achieved.

These days it is fashionable to try to set outcomes in very specific terms in relation to the changes achieved or visible products accomplished. Your statement may need to be refined or modified as you discuss it with colleagues and with potential group members. Initially you need to be sufficiently clear about what you want to achieve to be able to say something about possible outcomes. (See Application Exercises overleaf.)

Leadership and staffing

Who is to lead the group? (The terms 'group leader' and 'reminiscence worker' are used inter-changeably)

Is there to be one leader or co-leaders?

What preparation time will the leader(s) have?

Will the leader(s) have any supervision of their groupwork?

If so, who will provide it and under what circumstances?

GUIDANCE

Leading a group is a big responsibility for a single worker, especially if he or she is inexperienced. Try to find a co-leader. Decide if the leaders are to be managers or care staff or a combination of both. Often a staff member paired with a volunteer brings a welcome blend of familiarity and novelty, of security and new horizons. Make sure, whoever it is, that the leaders are likely to be

APPLICATION EXERCISES

1 Write down three statements beginning:

At the end of this reminiscence group's life I would like it to have achieved:

a _____

b _____

c _____

2 An alternative approach would be to write down:

At the end of this reminiscence group's life I would like the members to have achieved:

a _____

b _____

c _____

3 Writing competency statements about what you expect you will have learned to do is now also common:

At the end of this reminiscence group's life I shall be able to:

a _____

b _____

c _____

4 Write a simple explanation of the group's purpose which you could use when you invite potential members to join:

For example: 'I would like to form a reminiscence group which will provide you and X (a number) other residents/members with a chance to share your recollections of your past lives with each other so that you might value your past experience and find things you have in common with each other.'

'I would like to invite you to join a reminiscence group which will ...'

able to work amicably together. More information on co-working is contained in Chapter 7.

Co-leaders need time and opportunity to develop trust, confidence and respect for each other. If leaders or co-leaders are new to a facility, they will need to take time to familiarise themselves and to meet relevant staff and potential group members. To compete with each other is disastrous. Roles and responsibilities need to be clearly assigned and may be rotated. Take time outside the actual group meetings to plan together and to review each session. Do not say this is an unnecessary luxury and there is no time. Preparation and review or de-briefing are essential for successful co-working. Evaluation of the whole experience once the group is finished is also important, but is seldom easy to achieve. Sometimes this task is undertaken by an independent person, someone who has not been involved in the group. Evaluation means trying to reach a judgement about the value of the group, considering as far as possible both the tangible and intangible costs and benefits involved.

In addition to de-briefing, group workers find that the best way to develop their skills is to discuss their work with someone who is not directly involved in the group. This gives an opportunity to look very critically at what happened, how you felt, how you reacted and what you might do differently next time. Such stock-taking is not just for trouble-shooting but for building confidence and developing skills as well. Usually this supervisor will be a line manager but it could also be someone outside the workplace who is an experienced groupwork consultant.

Membership and invitations

Is the group to have open or closed membership?

How big should the group be?

Who should decide who is to be invited?

Who is to be invited?

Who is to do the inviting?

How are people to be invited?

Will it be possible to meet potential members individually?

GUIDANCE

An open group means that the group continues even if the members change over time. In open groups members join and leave at any time. This means that some members are always at the beginning stage. The development of group identity and cohesion is continually being set back. Longer-standing members may be frustrated and new members may feel like interlopers. In these circumstances relationships do not have the same opportunity to develop.

Some settings, however, determine the nature of the group. For example, groups in hospital acute wards, assessment units or respite care facilities where most people are there for only a short time have to be open. A common experience where everyone is facing the same uncertainties associated with crisis or transition may compensate to some extent for the difficulties associated with open membership. Groups where some members leave and others remain for the duration of the group are particularly difficult to lead.

Closed membership means that all the group members join at the beginning and are expected to remain for the agreed life of the group. Illness, death or other emergencies may mean that some people are absent or leave but in a closed group they are not replaced by a new member.

Closed groups move through the stages from tentative beginnings to established middles to anticipated endings. If handled skilfully by the leaders, these groups give the members a valued, satisfying experience of unified purpose, acceptance, intimacy, respect, development over time and a sense of achievement.

Group size Groups doing general reminiscence work are probably best limited to eight to twelve members. More experienced leaders may be able to manage larger groups but these should not be confused with large-scale nostalgic recreational activities. Participating in these large events is a different experience from the planned small groupwork advocated here.

Special reminiscence work is best done with far fewer people – most frequently with individuals. Chapter 8 suggests that reminiscence with people with dementia requires very small groups, usually with no more than two to four members, and individual work is often more productive than groupwork. Reminiscence with people who are depressed also requires special modifications, which are discussed in Chapter 9.

People with hearing, sight or speech problems find it very difficult to participate actively in groups unless special arrangements (such as those described in Chapter 10) are possible.

Invitations Questions about who is to be invited to join a reminiscence group are best discussed in staff meetings so that consensus can be achieved. It is sometimes helpful to use natural groupings if these already exist. For example, a key worker might run a group for the residents for whom she has special responsibility. Try to identify other groupings such as people who once lived in the same neighbourhood, worked in the same occupation, came from the same place, followed the same sporting interests or shared a common experience such as immigration, bereavement or illness. Select people who are likely to feel comfortable with each other and who will enjoy each other's company, rather than feel isolated or embarrassed.

Sometimes the staff may wish to use a group to integrate people, for example a newcomer or an isolated, solitary person. A reminiscence group may then be used to encourage mixing in the hope that it may help new relationships to develop.

> **Care assistant** 'In my Home the men and women always sat in different rooms. They seldom mixed with each other. We agreed to hold the reminiscence group in the women's lounge and Mr Smith said at the end of the first meeting how much he had enjoyed visiting another part of the Home. He said it was better than having an outing!'

It is usually best if the group leaders issue the invitations. Sometimes a key worker or a member of staff who has a special relationship with a person might be better placed to do so. Whoever it is, they must extend a genuine free choice about participation. There are powerful hierarchies in most establishments. If powerful staff extend the invitation, some people may feel obliged to accept. What might look like freedom to staff may be perceived as pressure by residents.

There is no one best way of either selecting or inviting group members. Wherever you work, the guiding principle must be open staff discussion. Sometimes a public invitation on a notice board or in a news sheet works well. You may then need to think in terms of size and mix of members. If you have more people respond than is manageable, make sure that there are further opportunities which people are kept informed about.

Staff often think they know best who is suitable and unsuitable for reminiscence groupwork. Sometimes they deny opportunities to people, especially those who are different or have special needs. Keep an open mind rather than reach hasty decisions. Give people an opportunity to decide for themselves.

If you are an inexperienced groupworker it is unwise to overload a group with too many people with special problems. Initially, people may not understand what is meant by a reminiscence or memories group. Some people will be reluctant to try anything that sounds new or strange. These same people may soon want to join, once word has got around that the group is interesting – a resident who first refused an invitation later announced, as she 'squatted' in the reminiscence room, 'I know what you are doing in here and I'm coming!'

For your first group, try to select some natural storytellers who will help the discussion along. If the group goes well, your confidence will quickly grow, and in your next group you will be able to be more adventurous about whom to include.

Personal interviews Each person who is to be invited, or who responds to a general invitation, should be seen before the first meeting. You can then explain about the group, gather some details about their past life and ask what themes or topics they would like the group to discuss.

A Personal History Form to assist you to collect and organise preliminary biographical information is given in Appendix 1.

People are usually ambivalent, if not fearful about committing themselves to a new experience, so you need to use this personal interview as a bridge into the group. Be clear about the nature of the invitation, sensitive to any fear or anxiety, and show genuine respect for the person's hopes and expectations for the group.

This initial meeting contributes to the 'contract' or 'working agreement' you will make with the group, so you need to be able to explain the group in simple, straightforward language. Understanding about the objectives or expected outcomes will grow and develop as the group develops. This preliminary meeting, however, is very important in securing initial consent and in making the potential member feel that joining the group is worth risking.

Some care staff think that because they see the potential members every day as they go about their ordinary work, they do not need to take the time to gather initial background information. This is a mistake. Remember that the success of any group is closely linked to the attention given to planning and preparation.

The lifetime of the group

How often should the group meet?

Will it be time-limited or open-ended?

If time-limited, for how many weeks will it meet?

GUIDANCE

Some groups, especially those who see themselves more as local history groups rather than reminiscence groups, are likely to be open-ended and to continue, probably with changing membership, for as long as people wish. They are more like a club or a class. Some continue for many years.

It is customary for formed reminiscence groups to meet for a set number of sessions, usually six to ten. Because it takes a group time to develop through the different phases, fewer than six sessions is likely to mean that the group experience will be much more limited and less satisfying. At least ten sessions are desirable but be realistic about what you can hope to sustain.

Once-a-week meetings are conventional but task-centred groups working on a specific project may wish to meet more frequently. Groups for people with dementia usually meet more often than once-weekly. It is usually better to stick to the agreed number and frequency of sessions rather than let a time-limited group drift on. Finish as planned and then begin preparation for your next group. Sometimes groups decide to transform themselves in terms of type of membership and the time span over which they intend to operate, but it is better for this transformation to be explicitly recognised by the group at some point.

Meeting arrangements

Where will the group meet?

What time of day is best for meetings?

How long will a meeting last?

Who will help the members gather together and disperse?

Who will sit next to whom?

Where will the leader(s) sit?

GUIDANCE

Location Make sure you choose a venue that is available for each meeting, comfortable, warm, informal and relaxed, and free from interruptions. Try not to intrude on other people's 'space', especially if they are not to be included as group members. Such invasions can create resentment. People displaced from their regular sitting areas and favourite chairs may try to assert their territorial rights by gate-crashing.

By holding the group in an unfamiliar place such as an underused staff room, a feeling of excitement and adventurousness can be generated. Hospital wards, short of small rooms and quiet, private day space, present particular challenges. It is sometimes possible, in spite of obvious distractions, to hold a small group around the bedside of a person who is unable to get up.

Duration and timing Meetings vary in length according to the physical and mental fitness of the members. About an hour is usual. Additional time needs to be allowed for gathering together, dispersing and having refreshments. In each session it takes time for the group to gather, settle, warm to the work, then to wind down, end the session, and disperse. Try not to be rushed yourself or to rush others.

Think carefully about the best time of day for a group meeting. This will vary from place to place depending on staff rotas, meal times, other activities, care routines and transport arrangements in day care. Find a time that causes least hassle for everyone involved and stick to it. The agreed time for the agreed number of sessions should be honoured. In these ways the staff demonstrate their commitment to the contract and their respect for the work they and the members are doing together.

Escorting Be sure you have made a clear plan about responsibility for helping members gather and disperse if they are unable to get themselves to the meeting place. Gathering together frail people can be complicated and time-consuming. A co-leader may undertake this task or share it with other staff. Everyone involved will need to understand the importance of timekeeping. Forgetful members will need to be reminded on the day of the meeting.

Seating The job of the leader is to make it possible for all the members to participate, so think carefully about how you arrange the room, including the positioning of each chair. Try to use the accommodation in whatever way is most likely to encourage the members to talk to each other, not just to the leaders.

Think about where members may prefer to sit and which arrangements would be most likely to help them feel secure and encourage participation. People may overcome their initial anxiety by sitting next to a friend, spouse or familiar person. As the group develops into the middle phase they may be more prepared to take other seats. Anyone with a sight or hearing difficulty, who needs special help if they are to participate fully, is best sat near a leader. If you have more than one leader, disperse yourselves. Do not cluster together to bolster your own confidence!

Programme

What themes or topics will the group discuss?

How will these themes be organised or arranged?

What triggers might be used?

How will these triggers be obtained?

What equipment will be needed?

Who will manage the equipment?

Will refreshments be part of the group meeting?

If so, who will be responsible for providing them?

GUIDANCE

Themes The choice of themes or topics for discussion must rest in the hands of the group members. The leader may propose topics but should defer to the group because, in this style of groupwork, the group belongs to the members. The leader helps the group turn its ideas into a logical and consistent programme which will achieve the agreed objectives. By reading, watching films or videos or visiting museums, group leaders can familiarise themselves with the broad historical period in which the group members have lived. Through such preparation they will be better able to understand the recollections of group members.

Some examples of possible themes are given in Chapter 5. The leader(s) chooses the content and plans the first session bearing in mind what has been found out about people's interests in the preliminary interviews. The subsequent sessions need to be planned, at least in outline, by the group, and part of the ending work of each session is to plan the next session.

There is no limit to the type or range of subjects that can be discussed. The programme may be based on topics, themes or subjects, or it may follow a chronological order, dealing with different historical periods or life stages. Themes are usually easier for inexperienced workers to manage. Each theme may have within it many different topics which can be developed over a number of sessions. If you strike a rich vein, with the group's agreement, build on it in future sessions. For example: a session on foreign holidays could be followed up with sessions on working abroad, foreign food, money, clothes, music, souvenirs, films, important buildings, housing, and friends and acquaintances from other countries.

Whether a thematic or chronological approach is used, it is always important to follow the interests and life experiences of the members. Do not impose your own preferences.

> **Reminiscence worker** 'I was really interested in the London blitz because my mother had been in it and I wanted the group to talk about that. When I suggested this they said: "No. None of us was in London during the war. Let's talk about weddings – they are nice and cheerful"; and I had to let them.'

Triggers These need to appeal to all the senses of sight, sound, touch, taste and smell because different people respond in different ways. They can speed up the time needed within a session to achieve warm engagement and mutual sharing of experience. In some groups triggers are not necessary.

Try to build up your own small collection of multi-sensory triggers. Collect, beg and borrow objects from everyday work and domestic life, not grand antiques. Many useful items can be found in junk shops, market stalls, car boot sales and in the attics or cupboards of older relatives. For a small outlay it is easy to pick up secondhand books and magazines, old kitchen gadgets, tools, tins, boxes, cards, coins and household articles. Friends and staff are usually very willing to lend things once they understand their potential usefulness.

Music and other sounds are especially good for evoking memories. Recordings of once-familiar sounds such as the whistle from a steam train, children playing, a school bell ringing, or the clip-clop of a dray horse can arouse instant recollections. Smells can stimulate memories, particularly those associated with food and home-baking. For more information about using music in reminiscence work, see pages 66–67 and 115–116.

Many people enjoy seeing pictures or projected slides. Reading aloud stories or poems from old newspapers, books, comics and magazines is very effective. Handling and examining objects, noting their colours, shapes and textures, debating their uses, quite apart from the associated recollections they evoke, can be very enjoyable.

Live triggers such as a baby, small child or animal can immediately generate interest, even in the most passive people. Plants, twigs, bark, leaves, grass, pine cones, fruit, vegetables and flowers can all be used.

Other examples of multisensory triggers are given in Chapter 5.

Libraries, local museums, local historical societies, community groups, local newspapers and photographic archives are all potential resources. Triggers are readily available once you begin to look around and see the possibilities in things you have long taken for granted.

Many trigger packages containing tapes, slides and photographs can be bought. These off-the-shelf trigger materials are useful if you are very busy and do not have much time for preparation. Without doubt, they have helped to make reminiscence work popular. On the other hand, if you rely on them too much or use them in a mechanical, routine way, reminiscence work will degenerate into nothing more than nostalgic entertainment or just something you feel obliged to do.

It is much better to start with people, not triggers. Discover their interests and concerns and then look for triggers that closely match. Always begin with the people, not the triggers.

Equipment If you use tape recorders, film projectors or video recorders, be sure you know how to work them. You will soon grow in confidence and master the technology, but if you are inexperienced, do practise. Taking turns to be responsible for this aspect of a group session spreads the expertise.

If you intend to show 35-mm slides in daylight, most projectors require reduced light so curtains will be necessary. An extension lead, a table or stand of the required height and either a blank wall, preferably white, or a screen will also be needed. Pre-loading projectors are preferable. Slides have to be loaded back to front and upside down. The room will need to be darkened but not blacked out completely. Retain some light if possible and sit people in a semi-circle. Be sure that everyone can see the screen, but bear in mind that a semi-circle makes member-to-member conversation much more difficult than a full circle.

Projectors with cooling fans hum, making hearing more difficult. So once the group has had a good look at the picture, you may want to switch the projector off for a time. In any case, slides can be damaged if they are exposed to the heat of a projector for too long.

Portable 35-mm slide presenters which incorporate a tape recorder are useful but expensive. They project either a small picture about the size of a small TV screen (front projection) or else a large picture suitable for a screen or wall (back projection). They are very useful for taking to a person's bedside or to somebody's own home. Slide presenters can also be used for making your own synchronised tape/slide programmes if you want to put together your own local trigger materials.

A camera can greatly enhance the work of a reminiscence group. It can be used for taking photographs for stimulating 'then and now' discussions and for producing material for displays and exhibitions. It is also a great asset in individual life story work.

A tape recorder for playing and recording sounds, music and recollections is a useful piece of equipment. They vary greatly in type, price and ease of use. Cassette recorders are simple to use. There is a lot to learn about making good sound recordings but there is no need to be intimidated. Get advice, do some reading and then make a start. Tapes of group members' recollections can be used as triggers in future sessions. In this way each group becomes a potential resource for future work.

Multi media CD-ROMs, e-mail and the Internet are beginning to be used by computer-literate older people. Many software programmes have great potential to stimulate reminiscence, assist recall and link people in new and exciting ways. Archiving local or personal photographic and documentary resources is already possible using computer software such as the Comma programme produced by Polkaville (see Appendix 3).

Before buying any audio/visual or computer equipment, seek independent advice from someone who is technically knowledgeable but who does not have a vested interest in selling a particular brand or model.

Make friends with the staff at your local public library. They can assist in innumerable ways. Many local libraries and sound archives lend recorders, projectors, cassettes, CDs, videos, and sometimes pictures, as well as printed material. Increasingly they are providing access to the Internet.

Refreshments served either before or, preferably, at the end of a session make the group meeting special. Once-familiar food, especially taking the preferences and past experience of people from other cultures into account, can be enormously evocative and can become part of the whole reminiscence experience.

Be clear about who is responsible for bringing the refreshments and for clearing them away. The timing is also important. Try hard to get the arrangements agreed in terms of the needs of the group, rather than the routines of the domestic staff.

Care assistant 'It was after we had turned off the projector, put down the things we had been passing around and the tea arrived that the real chat began. I have never seen the group so animated and excited. Even Mrs Upta was joining in. I do think it was the refreshments which helped to relax them and encouraged them to talk.'

Record keeping and confidentiality

Are the group discussions to be kept confidential?

Is there to be any feedback and, if so, to whom?

What records will be kept?

Who will write them?

Who will have access to them?

GUIDANCE

As part of preparation, leaders will need to have thought about record keeping and confidentiality so that in the first session some rules can be agreed. The arrangements will vary from group to group, but it is important that they are always openly agreed and understood.

Usually, to be strictly bound by confidentiality defeats the purpose of a reminiscence group. You want the mutual pleasure, personal achievement and group satisfaction to be widely communicated. Sometimes, however, when a group member has disclosed a very intimate or private recollection, the leader may need to contract with the group about treating that particular episode as confidential.

You may say:

'Mrs G__ has just trusted us with a very private memory. I suggest we all agree to regard it as confidential and not tell anyone outside the group what we have just been told. What do you think? Is that agreed by us all?'

You need to agree generally with the group about leaders being free to discuss group sessions with a colleague or consultant if you are being supervised by someone else. Do not assume that group members understand that staff members may be accountable to line managers for their work. Explain what the arrangements are in the place where you work.

Record forms Whether you are obliged to keep records for supervision or not, it is still a good idea to do so because it helps you reflect on the work you are doing, week by week, and to evaluate it at the end. Examples of record forms are given in Appendix 1.

Agree who is to write any records and who will have access to them. Records should be kept in a safe place. At the very least, keep an attendance record and follow-up any absentees. A good way of improving your groupwork skills is to make a 'process' record of any parts of a group session which went either very well or very badly. Try to remember exactly and write down accurately what triggered these 'critical incidents', who said what, the emotions expressed or withheld, and how you and your co-leader responded. When a group is over decide what is to be done with the records.

Property rights

Who 'owns' any tangible outcomes or products from the group?

To what agreed use might such outcomes be put?

Who benefits financially from any publications or sales arising from the group's work?

GUIDANCE

It may seem strange to be wondering about 'property rights' before your group has even met. This is, however, an ethical issue you need to think about. If you hope that the group might publish, exhibit or in some way make a record of its members' recollections, the group will need to agree and to give permission.

If life stories, photos, video recordings or personal memorabilia are to be used outside the group, it is a wise precaution to ask members to sign a simple release form at an appropriate time (see Appendix 1 for an example). People are seldom reluctant to publish but you must not take agreement for granted. Written permission is strongly recommended. Some people find it hard to believe that their lives are worth putting into print or that their experience could possibly interest anyone else. Even a modest document produced on a personal computer and photocopier can give its author enormous pleasure, pride and satisfaction.

Conclusion

This has been a long chapter but you were warned at the outset that success depends on careful preparation. Use this chapter as an aid to memory. For each new group, use the chapter as a checklist and make brief notes about what you need to do before you begin your first group session. Try not to think that because you have run a previous group you can skimp the preparations for a new one!

KEY POINTS

■ Take time over detailed preparation. It will pay off in the long run.

■ The group belongs to the members; not to you. You are an enabler, not an owner.

■ Do not avoid problems, hoping they will go away. They won't. They will go underground instead, waiting to sabotage you when least expected. So bring them into the open.

■ Learn to begin with people. Build a collection of multi-sensory triggers around their interests.

■ Develop the habit of keeping records of your work to help you develop the different skills required at different phases throughout the life of the group.

APPLICATION EXERCISE

Plan a reminiscence group, using the checklist to help guide you through the preparation phase.

Further Reading

Using Reminiscence: A training pack by Faith Gibson, Help the Aged, London, 1989:

> Part I *An Introduction*. Tape/slide presentation with transcript.
> Part II *Processes in a Small Group*. 48-minute video with transcript and teaching points.
> Part III *Individual and Groupwork: A manual.*

5   How to Run a Reminiscence Group

This chapter includes:

- The beginning phase of a group
- The middle phase of a group
- The ending phase of a group
- Using multi-sensory triggers
- Examples of topics or themes

Beginning phase of a group

Having completed the planning and preparation phase to the best of your ability, you are now ready for the group to meet. The first meeting of a new group needs to affirm everyone's best hopes, not confirm their worst fears. 'Tune in' to how you are feeling and try to imagine how the members may be feeling as the first meeting gets under way.

Members will probably be feeling much the same as you, both fearful and expectant. They will be ambivalent, torn in two directions at the same time. They will be worried about embarking on a new experience, especially if they have not previously belonged to a formed group. They will wonder what will be expected of them; will they be able to cope; will they be pressured into talking when they would prefer to remain silent; and will they be overshadowed, or perhaps overwhelmed, by dominating, talkative people?

At the same time as being fearful, they will be looking forward to a new experience; possibly meeting new people; hearing about new things; and wanting to share some of their own past experience and to have it valued and validated by others.

In order to overcome any initial anxiety, be present when the new members begin to arrive so that you can greet each person by name, making them feel welcome in whatever way is most appropriate.

Depending on whether or not members already know each other, the leader needs to make introductions. Some groups begin by having each member introduce themselves. This sometimes works well because it involves everyone, but it can be very daunting for a shy person to have to speak up right at the beginning.

Use people's preferred name – never a name that the leader assumes a right to use. People should be asked what they prefer to be called at the initial interview and their wishes respected. In making introductions, do nothing that might show up anyone's poor memory, or embarrass them in any way.

Follow the introductions with a brief statement about why you are all meeting together, and what you hope the group will accomplish. This introduction repeats the initial explanation you made and the tentative contract you agreed when you met members individually. If you did not have the chance to meet people beforehand, the introductions must be very clear and you need to 'reach for feedback' to make sure the members understand and agree about the purpose of the group.

A simple opening statement from the leader might be:

'We have agreed to meet today and for X weeks at Z time to talk about past times and to share our recollections with each other. We think we shall all benefit by talking about the past and today we have agreed we shall talk about Y. At the end of today's session we shall make plans for the other meetings. Is that all right with you all?'

This 'contracting' work is very important because it makes the members feel that the group genuinely belongs to them. It also means that in future meetings, if anyone wants to use the group for some other purpose, such as planning a fundraising event for example, you can return to this agreement, review it and agree if it still represents members' wishes, or in what ways it should be modified.

Leaders find it very hard to 'reach for feedback' at the beginning. This is because you will be anxious that the arrangements you have worked so hard to make at the planning and preparation stage might be upset, and your plans undermined.

Do not be afraid of trusting the group. A group has to be mutually satisfying to be successful. It never will be if you insist on working to your own agenda rather than the group's. Let everyone talk who wishes to. Such open questions as 'Is everyone agreeable to this?', 'Is everyone happy with these plans?' or 'Does someone have another idea?' indicate a genuine desire for the group to be founded on mutuality, with everyone sharing and participating as equally as possible.

Some leaders like to agree ground rules to try to help a group discipline itself but if this is done too early or too insensitively, it may make the leader look like a bossy teacher rather than an enabler or facilitator. This may happen anyway if the leader is a senior member of staff, already known to group members as the 'boss', because all groups actually start long before the first meeting to which people bring their prior experience and preconceptions.

A leader might say:

'Do you think it might be helpful if we agreed a few simple rules amongst ourselves so that everyone gets a chance to join in?' Seek feedback. 'Is that alright?' Then continue: 'I don't want to sound like the referee but it may help if we agree that everyone who wants to talk should get a chance to do so. Could we agree that only one person speaks at a time so everyone can hear? Is that okay? I suggest that we should respect different points of view, and not use unkind, hurtful or offensive language. We need to accept that old memories might bring up strong feelings. We might get a bit emotional at times. No one needs to feel embarrassed if this happens. We also need to talk about confidentiality. Maybe we should take these points one at a time... What do you think? ... Are these suggestions okay?'

It is a mistake to use the first session exclusively for planning. Although some time must be spent on this, be sure to do some reminiscing so that members leave with a feeling of excitement and a first-hand flavour of what they have come together to do. Otherwise they will be disappointed and puzzled. An opportunity for the group to grow together through shared work will have been lost.

Each session has a beginning, middle and end which should guide the leader's behaviour. So when the introductions have been completed, introduce the first topic or the first trigger by asking a simple question such as 'What does this remind you of?' or 'What does this take you back to?' Follow the pace and mood of the group. Do not worry if the discussion seems untidy or disjointed. It usually takes two or three sessions for a group to settle down, for everyone to feel comfortable, sufficiently confident to initiate discussion or to listen patiently to other people. Be finely tuned to the emotions being expressed, not just the words. Reach out to anyone who looks uncomfortable or upset and value everyone's contribution.

Watch the time. Stick to the agreed arrangements because if you do not, others will probably be inconvenienced. As the time gets close for ending the session the leader should begin ending work by reminding the members that time is nearly over for today, briefly summarise what has been done and suggest the group makes plans for its next meeting. Every small detail about all future sessions does not need to be agreed but the broad directions do.

For example, the leader may say:

'Time is nearly up for today but we still have X meetings left. You remember that we agreed that we might possibly talk about A, B or C. What would you like to cover next meeting?' After an agreement has been reached, check it out. Ask: 'Is that all right? Are you all happy with that suggestion?'

Reminiscence groups sometimes have a habit of starting again after you think a session has ended! Do not be worried about this. Animated conversation may continue outside the group session and involve others. This does not matter provided that agreements about confidentiality are honoured. Shared reminiscence can be very infectious and members' enthusiasm is the best advertisement.

Each subsequent session should begin with a modified form of group contracting and end by spending time setting the scene for the next meeting. Every group is dynamic – it grows and develops over time, so you will need to help it be responsibly flexible. Agreements or contracts are not strait-jackets which should never be modified. On the other hand, a group needs unity and order if it is not to be a free for all, at the mercy of the member with the loudest voice.

Many inexperienced leaders worry about 'losing control'. They imagine that somehow the group will run away from them, people will either talk too much or talk too little and that good order all depends on the leader. Such worries are diminished if you realise that you are a part of the group and that, although you have special responsibilities, the group belongs to everyone in it, not to the leaders.

People behave differently at different stages. Do be patient. In the beginning phase, most members (and leaders) are anxious. Some will talk a great deal and appear to be very domineering. This is often a cover for insecurity. Others will retreat into silence and yet resent the seemingly confident talkative members, even though such dominance saves the quieter person from having to talk.

In the beginning, members tend to talk more to the leader than to each other. Friends and acquaintances may talk to each other and to people sitting next to them but they may seem to ignore, or not be interested in, what other members have to say. People may lack the confidence to talk to the whole group but they settle down in time and there are ways of helping everyone feel more comfortable.

Using triggers in the early sessions (see examples given later in this chapter) can bolster an inexperienced leader's confidence. Triggers usually quickly arouse the interest of the group members and get conversation flowing. Early triggers should relate to the broad known life experience of as many of the group members as possible and not be restricted to a single member. They should not relate to potentially intimate, painful or private experience. Topics and triggers should not trap people into too early or too intimate disclosure.

If you want to encourage a silent or shy group member to participate, you can deliberately select triggers that relate very closely to
them and which they recognise and understand. In this way you
may very gently lead them into talking and sharing.

Give people time to develop trust in each other before you expect
them to share recollections of painful, divisive or very personal
experiences. This will come once the group has developed trust or
intimacy in the middle phase of work.

Middle phase of a group

After two or three meetings, the group moves into the middle
phase. It begins to feel less tentative, more sure of what it is doing,
more cohesive. During this stage, trust, respect and courtesy gradually emerge, people learn to attend to and respect each other. The
talkative, dominating member usually learns to listen and the quiet,
shy member, feeling valued, begins to talk.

Even the type of questions a leader asks can encourage or discourage
discussion. Learn the difference between an open and a closed question. The first provides choice about the response. The second
restricts choice. Avoid questions that have a right or wrong answer.
Do not ask questions which require a precise or factually correct
answer. For example, 'What year were you married?' or 'How many
children did you have?' are closed questions. If people lack confidence, they will not risk getting the answer wrong. Open questions,
like 'Tell us about your wedding', invite responses that other members can add to, embroider and develop from their own experience.

Leaders need to learn to be aware simultaneously of the group as
a group and also of all the individual members. This may seem a
tall order but it is possible with practice. Use eye contact, lean
towards people, nod to encourage the silent members to contribute but do not pressure them to do so. One simple trigger, or
just a short open-ended question may be sufficient to start people
talking but triggers that stimulate different senses in sequence are
powerfully evocative.

As the leader, do not regard yourself as the historical authority. You are an enabler whose task is to encourage the members to talk to each other. They are the authorities and the teachers. If the focus from the outset is on the members' own life experience, then obviously they are the experts. Your responsibility is to help them make connections between their own experience and the experience of other members.

Inexperienced leaders often use too many triggers. They seem determined to use everything they have prepared, even if discussion is flowing freely. Try not to be driven by an urge to stick to your own agenda. You have to be both orderly and responsive. You need to follow the flow and feelings of the group. Respect its timings, preoccupations and moods. Do not rush or pressure people but also be alert to possible boredom, restlessness or resistance.

Sometimes your best-laid plans can go astray, as this worker found:

> **Leader** 'Because the slide projector wasn't available we used two large pictures as trigger material. One of a shop and the other of the inside of a country cottage. Although I was worried about having to change my plans and the amount of time ahead, I was pleasantly surprised to find the group members taking great enjoyment in talking about every detail in these pictures. As Mr K talked I could see a transformation taking place. The members changed from passive observers with very brief comments to excited participants who could not wait to talk about churning, milking and local creameries.'

Members may begin risking stories which have layers of meaning. They may try out different versions according to how they 'read' or perceive their present audience. Some may feel sufficiently safe to talk about painful recollections. Others may be reluctant to do so, frightened of their own pain and perhaps of being left worse off, rather than better off, as a result of allowing a long buried hurt to resurface.

Leaders need to be particularly alert to loss in all its many guises. No one grows old without experiencing repeated loss. It may be of loved ones, family, friends and relations. There may be diminished energy, loss of health, of cherished possessions, special places and once-absorbing interests. As loss emerges and people face the inevitable comparisons between their past and present circumstances, resistance is unavoidable and becomes part of the work. Some members may want to talk whilst others may be afraid to listen because they fear being overwhelmed by the pain aroused in themselves by hearing other people's recollections.

Many leaders find it hard to encourage reminiscence groups to share pain. In a million ways they damp it down, choke it off and keep the conversation superficial. Learn to overcome your own reluctance to share another's hurt. Point the group members towards each other and make links between their experience. They can become a rich resource for each other. They will probably know more about sharing loss than you do, so use their vulnerability and their strength to help the whole group.

Emotion will never be far from the surface in any reminiscence group. Quickly the mood can change from gaiety to sadness, from laughter to tears. Do not be afraid of tears nor think you have done harm if people cry.

A member may recall very painful past experience, and the recall may bring distress and also relief, in that it may be the first time such memories have been shared with others.

Learn to respect silences. Do not be embarrassed nor hurry people on. People need time if they are getting in touch with deeply felt emotions. It is not a time for rush or bustle or false jokes. Most of us dread silence and hurry to fill the space with idle chatter. Learn to wait out the silence, then to name it and then to link the experience and the emotion of the individual with the experience and feelings of the rest of the group members. The group is the resource. Use it to the full, but be aware that follow-up outside the group may also be necessary.

A few members may never talk or they may talk very little but their body language will indicate how they feel about the group. Try to understand what the experience means for each individual and enable them to use the group in whichever way best meets their needs.

Great sensitivity is needed when members begin bringing in their own triggers. This can be particularly significant for them but it can also heighten a sense of loss or isolation for others. To see others contributing personal cherished possessions may increase their feelings of separation or dislocation from their past.

During the lifetime of a group, energy and involvement will vary from meeting to meeting. Over time, if members seem to lose interest, do not just silently deplore this or feel hurt. Try to understand what is happening and openly address the issue. Confronting is a very necessary skill in groupwork but it is one that leaders are often reluctant to use. Confrontation must never be threatening to people, the powerful leader imposing his or her own will on the powerless group member. Confrontation is not combative. It is honestly facing up to a problem, having open discussion about it and jointly agreeing how to proceed.

If the group is a formed group with closed membership and a member is absent, this should be acknowledged in the session. Any absences should be followed up and explained to the other members. Sometimes people change their minds about participating, deciding that reminiscence is not for them. Such views should always be respected but make sure that there is no other hidden negative reason for a person withdrawing which requires remedial action by the leader.

In groups with open membership which changes from meeting to meeting, group intimacy may never be achieved although individuals may still find the experience constructive. Each meeting will need to be self-contained because continuity of participants and programme will not be possible. Such groups will probably rely more on triggers, less on spontaneous exchange of personal experience, and will depend more on the leader for active direction.

As the length of time spent in hospital decreases, and respite care and short-term admissions increase, formed groups with closed membership may be more and more difficult to sustain except in community settings. Do not assume that groups in residential or nursing homes will work in the same way as groups in day centres. You need to be alert to each distinctive context of care, its particular constraints and opportunities, and to modify your reminiscence groupwork accordingly.

Ending phase of a group

In time-limited groups which meet for an agreed number of sessions, it is usual to foreshadow the end of the group from the beginning, as already mentioned. Each week members can be reminded of how many sessions remain. In this way the ending is anticipated from the outset. Endings, like beginnings, are a time of increased opportunity for work because they are a time when feelings are more exposed. Groups that have been successful, that have worked well together and shared much, end with less pain than those which have never really 'got going'.

Even in successful groups, members will experience mixed emotions around endings. Some may feel relieved that the group is over. Others may resent that it is not continuing, or feel sad or angry that they must face another 'ending'. Leaders may feel pleased with their achievements or guilty because more was not accomplished. Probably everyone involved will experience a mixture of these emotions.

In the ending phase, leaders have a big responsibility to make sure that the ending, with its mixed emotions, is openly addressed. Do not let your group just fade away, even if some members have anticipated its ending by ceasing to attend. Use part of the last session for stock-taking. Invite the members to look back, to acknowledge the work they have done together, and to say what the experience has meant for them.

Try not to be talked into extending the life of the group. You may be placed under considerable pressure to do so – 'just a few more sessions.' Stick to the contract but be open about how people, yourself included, feel because the group is ending.

Resist dealing with your own feelings by promising something in the future that you cannot deliver. If there is a realistic chance that there can be another reminiscence group, say so. Do not make promises you cannot keep. Pain faced is more constructive than pain denied.

Some groups try to handle their strong feelings around endings by giving themselves a farewell party which tends to emphasise the positives and ignore the pain of impending separation. Of course, there is a place for parties, special events and celebrations but if these are left until the final session, rich opportunities may be lost for building on a positive experience during the middle phase of the group. A shared outing or other special event at that stage could be relished, recalled and used subsequently as a basis for further work. The final meeting can still be special if it reviews and celebrates the work done.

If the group has agreed to produce a tangible product such as a publication or exhibition, make sure you deliver on this. Be clear about the time-scale and mutual responsibilities. On no account promise a product that you do not have resources to produce.

Roger Sim, a Hospital Arts worker, believes:

'It is important in any arts or reminiscence project to mark achievement with a celebration or ceremony – both to thank and acknowledge all those who have been involved and also to attract the attention of managers and those who may be in a position to resource future developments.'

Endings also mean that the leaders need to review and evaluate the work undertaken. Just as after each session it is important to spend a little time considering how the session went, so at the end you need to look back to reflect on all the work you and the group have done together. Review your notes from each session. Look back on what you said you hoped to achieve. Try to be realistic, do give yourself, co-leader, helpers and members credit for work accomplished as well as facing up to the things that could have been done differently, or done better.

Using multi-sensory triggers

Many different approaches can be used to encourage the sharing of memories and to encourage people with disabilities to participate. Both verbal and non-verbal communication are important in reminiscence work. Some groups may like to draw or paint, sometimes accompanied by music, to read, write or recite poems, sing, dance, act, tell stories, complete proverbs, do quizzes, make collages, mosaics or wallhangings, and draw maps or family trees. Many of these things are also appropriate for working with individuals. There is no limit to the possibilities, provided people freely agree, do not feel pressured and no individual is made to feel in any way inadequate, demeaned or deficient.

Visual triggers

Visual triggers are the most readily available and include photographs of people, places, things and events. There are three types of photographs: personal, artistic and documentary. Look for photographs that combine the personal and the documentary. Even if you want to use a picture of a particular place, one that portrays people and possibly action will be a more effective trigger than a beautiful lifeless scene. Use pictures of ordinary people doing ordinary things.

A professional picture of a great public occasion may not be nearly as effective as personal snapshots of reasonable quality. Pictures of public events, for example the Queen's coronation, the assassination of President Kennedy, or in years to come, Princess Diana's funeral, can be used for asking people: 'What were you doing on the day when ... ?'

You may be fortunate in locating a local public photographic collection or a private collection belonging to someone who has documented community changes over the years. Local photographers are often delighted to discover a 'therapeutic' use for their life-long hobby and willingly lend or copy their pictures.

There are many large public photographic collections in various parts of the UK. The best known is the Hulton Picture Company (formerly the Hulton Picture Library; see Appendix 3). You may need to go by appointment to view, or sometimes photocopies can be mailed to help you decide exactly what you want before ordering copies which may be very expensive and take several weeks to obtain.

Enlarging and mounting on laminated board will increase a photograph's usefulness and prolong its life. Several copies of the same picture enable group members to examine them closely and discuss them with each other. This is a useful technique if people have hearing, sight or speech difficulties.

Newspaper articles and advertisements may be photocopied and enlarged. Again, getting them laminated, mounted or put in plastic covers will extend their life. Plastic covers unfortunately reduce the impact of most pictures. Colour photocopying produces high quality copies cheaply and quickly.

Objects too precious to handle may be photographed. Pictures of many objects are readily available in commercial packages. Postcards, books, magazines and newspapers are another source. Local newspapers frequently publish photographs of past times with accompanying articles which are excellent for reading aloud. A reminiscence session may need little more than a local newspaper or an old advertisement to start discussion. Some commercial publishers and distributors of reminiscence materials are listed in Appendix 3.

The three *Recall*, tape/slide programmes with notes, long out of print, are still widely used and may be available from libraries. Several other packages modelled on *Recall* are available for different parts of the UK and Ireland. These packages require a 35-mm slide projector.

Slides, sound tapes or videos need to be used very selectively. They can encourage passive rather than active viewing if you let yourself become the captive of technology and lose the courage to turn the machinery off. Any aids or triggers must always be servants, not masters. Their purpose in reminiscence is to enable the group members to talk actively with each other, not just to sit passively watching or listening to yet another programme.

Historical video films should be used cautiously. A few minutes viewing may be sufficient to stimulate discussion. Some school history programmes are very useful. Film libraries and film archives are increasingly transferring films to video which require either a video presenter (a small all-in-one machine) or a video recorder and TV monitor. Do make sure beforehand that the video is properly tuned to the TV set and that you know how to work both.

Auditory triggers

Memory for sounds can be vivid and immediate. Usually a sound is associated in the mind's eye with a visual memory and it may be quite impossible to separate the two. By triggering one, both are triggered. Sound, provided people do not have a hearing problem, can be very evocative. Recordings of sounds are readily available on records, compact discs, videos and cassettes. They include music of all kinds and periods, sound effects recordings, stories, poetry, plays, autobiographies and documentaries. You may also want to make your own recordings. Local radio is a rich resource as the closer the sounds, speech and accents mirror people's own background, the richer will be the response.

Music is particularly effective because it speaks immediately to people's emotions. It captures attention while also being relaxing, making people feel at ease. It can be enjoyed in its own right and also for the associated memories it triggers. Locate music that reflects varied tastes and experiences. Get people to tell you what music they once enjoyed and would like to hear. Live musical performances are very popular. Identify talent within your own workplace or neighbourhood.

Try to provide opportunities for older people to keep up or renew their musical skills, or acquire new ones. Encourage active participation in music-making, including singing rhymes, hymns and songs or playing simple percussion instruments. But beware of making older people feel they are being patronised. There is a world of difference between recallng or re-enacting childhood experience and being treated as a child. Recorded music, song sheets and song books, including some with large print, are useful.

If you are doing group singing, give all group members a chance to suggest a song, even if they are not keen to join in the singing. Respect everyone's choice and make sure that no one feels embarrassed. Home would have been the focus for entertainment for most older people. Singing around the piano and listening to the radio or phonograph would only slowly have been replaced by television from the 1950s onwards. (See also pages 46 and 115–116 for more about using music in reminiscence work.)

Tactile triggers

Instant pleasure and immediate recall are triggered from handling objects. Just holding something, then passing it to the next person links people together and stimulates cumulative shared memories. Objects encourage demonstration of how they were used. They invite activity, shared opinion and animated conversation.

Try not to use objects that can only be admired from a distance. Use everyday items like working tools and household gadgets that people can handle and pass to each other without fear of damaging them. Strange objects encourage debate, even disagreement.

> **Day care worker** 'We had a dolly, which is a thing used for washing blankets, but hardly anyone knew what it was for. Someone said it was an ear trumpet. Another person said it was for clearing drains. There were the greatest arguments. Everyone joined in and enjoyed the fun.'

If you select triggers with care, over the weeks everyone's life experience can be represented in one way or another, and this encourages everyone to feel that their past has been acknowledged.

Tastes and smells as triggers

Even if these senses diminish with age, tastes and smells can still be used, either alone or combined in sequence with other triggers, to enrich a theme or explore a topic. It is very easy and inexpensive to make your own smell collection. Put the same substance or liquid into several matching small bottles or containers (empty camera film cartons, for example) which can be passed around among people who will very quickly start a guessing game when trying to identify the smell.

Similar and contrasting smells challenge people to identify, distinguish and name the smells as well as to discuss the associated memories which are stirred. Some possible smells include disinfectants, toiletries, medicines, herbs and spices, and flowers and other plants.

Reminiscing about favourite food, associated smells and related people and events can be easily encouraged. Reading stories aloud, looking at old recipe books, recalling food produced for special occasions, using packets, tins and packaging can all be helpful. The most immediate and richest recollections are achieved by actually serving and eating the food. Cooking old favourites can also involve other staff members in the reminiscence work. If it is possible, involve the group in food preparation, advice, instruction and recalling associated memories.

Reminiscence on the theme of food may be a way of reviving rusty cooking skills and rekindling or creating fresh interest in nutrition and personal care.

> **Care worker** 'We were talking in one session about summertime, gardening and fruit picking. This led on to what our mothers used to do with the fruit and we began to talk about making jam. Mrs Smith said how she wished she could still make plum jam and the group then decided they would like to do that, with everyone sharing a part of the job. We got a lot of help from the kitchen staff but everyone did something to help. We all had such fun. The best part was when everyone had scones for tea and ate our group's plum jam. We were so pleased with ourselves.'

A co-operative activity like this could be focused on many other cooking or household tasks such as butter-making or baking bread. It could also incorporate a trip to orchards, farms, gardens, shops or mills.

Examples of themes

- home life
- clothing
- washday and other housework
- wartime

- childhood
- school days
- work
- leisure

Any of these themes could be used for several sessions or just for one, depending on the interests of the group, the triggers available and whether the group might like to write or record its recollections. These could then be read aloud and used to link subsequent sessions. Many of the suggested triggers relate to more than one theme and its related topics.

You will see that each broad theme has many different topics within it. Only some of the many possible themes and topics with related multi-sensory triggers are listed to help get you started. Let your own imagination get to work. Discover the innumerable possibilities all around you.

HOME LIFE

Topics	Triggers
The street where you lived The house where you grew up Bathing and hair-washing Meeting people and making friends Courtship and marriage Childbirth Illness, home remedies and cures Death and funerals Christmas and other festivals Favourite food Recipes and cooking Shops and shopping Friends and neighbours	Photographs, maps, carbide lamp, torch, razor, shaving brush, nutmeg and grater, snuff, paraffin lamp, Jeyes fluid, moth balls, carbolic soap, shroud and bed linen, Vicks, camphor, cookery books, cards, curling tongs, pre-decimal money, photograph albums, Christmas decorations, flowers, plants, seed packets, seed catalogues, gardening tools and mail order catalogues

CLOTHING

Topics	Triggers
Fashion over 50–70 years Working clothes Best clothes Handing down and making do Footwear	Button hook, hat pins, corsets and stays, braces, hats, shoes, boots, shoe polish, lavender, mothballs, cosmetics, perfumes, jewellery, furs, apron, collar stud, tie pin, hats, shoelast, spats, stick-on soles, knitting patterns, wool, needles

WASHDAY AND OTHER HOUSEWORK

Topics	Triggers
Household appliances Wash day Starching and ironing Drying clothes Going to the launderette Mending, darning and sewing Saturday jobs	Wash tubs and board, dolly, knob of blue, Sunlight soap, flat iron, gas iron, electric iron, starch, feather duster, clothing, darning needle, early electrical appliances, sewing machine, cooking utensils, kitchen equipment

WARTIME

Topics	Triggers
World War I and II The day war was declared Evacuation, women's war work Air raids, fire-watching Rationing of food and clothing Americans and other servicemen Life in the armed forces ARP wardens and air raids Civilian work	Films and books, pictures, paintings, reading war poetry, letters and diaries, evacuation instructions, warden's helmet and arm band, ration book and coupons, identity card, service uniforms, medals, gas mask, recordings of Gracie Fields, Vera Lynn and other wartime music

CHILDHOOD

Topics	Triggers
Parents and grandparents	Conkers, skipping rope, rag doll,
Brothers and sisters	oil of cloves, brandy balls,
Rhymes, songs and riddles	aniseed, sherbet fountains,
Street games and pastimes	licorice, mint balls, paradise
Toys, books and comics	plums, gobstoppers, barley sugar,
What you did on a wet day	jelly babies, Dinky cars, comics,
How you spent Sunday	club badges, cigarette cards,
Visiting the sweet shop	china dolls, clockwork toys,
What work your parents did	tinplate and plastic toys,
Taking care of younger children	hopscotch tawes, teddy bears,
Clothes you used to wear	marbles, old money
Rewards and punishments	
Doing odd jobs and messages	
Pocket money	

SCHOOL DAYS

Topics	Triggers
Getting to school	Slate and pencil, chalk, reading
School and classrooms	book, copy book, exercise book,
What was kept in the desk	crayons, wall chart, jotters, ink,
Teachers, favourite lessons	ink-well, nib, pen, biro, text
First day at school	books, school photographs,
Learning to write	school clothes and uniforms,
What was kept in pencil case	school bag, badges, recording of
Lunchtime and break time	school bell, calling the roll,
Playground games and sports	reciting tables, reading poems
Truanting or mitching, gangs	and stories, singing, school
Secret places, best friend	reports, programmes from
Special occasions, speech day,	speech days and sports days
sports day	
Leaving school	

WORK

Topics	Triggers
My first job and how I got it	Pay-packet, lunch tin,
My first pay packet and how I	advertisements, train and bus
spent it	tickets, union card, job
People at work	advertisements, horseshoe, ears
Pay and working conditions	of wheat, corn, barley, hops,
Strikes and industrial unrest	tools, working clothes
Being unemployed	
Travelling to work	
Leaving home, going into digs	
Emigrating to seek work	
Rural work and town work	
Being apprenticed	
Domestic service	
Shop and office work	

LEISURE

Topics	Triggers
Going on day trips and holidays	Cinema ticket, chocolate box,
Cinema, music hall and theatre	ice cream wrappers,
Dancing and dance bands	programmes, postcards, holiday
Games and sporting events	snaps, bathing suits, beer mats,
Hobbies and pastimes	matchboxes, sand, shells, rock,
Pet animals and birds	sporting equipment, bus, train or
Evening at the pub or club	tram tickets, recordings of rock
Day at the beach, races, dogs	or jazz musicians
Public transport, bicycles, cars	
and motor bikes	
Package holidays	

Information about hiring and borrowing theme reminiscence boxes is given in Appendix 3. Some local museums and libraries offer similar services, but loan materials usually have to be collected and returned by the borrower.

KEY POINTS

- The first and last phases of a group are very important and provide great opportunities for work if handled well by the leader.
- It is important to learn to listen to people's pain and sadness.
- Only promise what you can deliver and make sure you deliver what you promise.
- Triggers that appeal to all the senses encourage shared recollections and lively discussion.
- Start with people, discover what might interest them and then locate relevant triggers.

APPLICATION EXERCISES

Undertake these exercises either on your own or with a potential co-leader:

1 Choose a theme or a topic and write a detailed work plan, listing preparations you will need to make and possible available triggers you would like to use. Identify any related activities and possible tangible products or outcomes.

2 Run the group you have planned.

3 After the group is finished, write a short closing statement summing up achievements for the group and for the leader(s).

a) 'The group achieved ...'

b) 'I (we) learned to ...'

c) 'I (we) need to continue to work on ...'

Further Reading

Groupwork with the Elderly by M Bender, A Norris and P Bauckham. Winslow, Bicester, 1987.

The Reminiscence Handbook: Ideas for creative activities with older people by C Osborn. Age Exchange, London, 1993.

6 Reminiscence with Individuals

This chapter includes:

- Spontaneous reminiscence and prompted or planned reminiscence
- Life review, reminiscence work and guided autobiographical writing
- Behaviours which challenge carers
- Methods used for recording and presenting reminiscence and life history work
- Some ethical considerations

Spontaneous and prompted reminiscence and various methods or approaches for working with individuals will be described. Using reminiscence with people with dementia, depression, hearing, sight and speech difficulties is discussed more fully in Chapters 8, 9 and 10, but much of this chapter is also relevant to reminiscence work with people who have such disabilities.

Spontaneous and prompted or planned reminiscence

Carers in institutions, day centres and in domiciliary care need to be alert to opportunities to value and encourage spontaneous reminiscence. Family carers should also be encouraged to do the same. Spontaneous recall by an individual may prompt others around them to begin reminiscing. Try to understand what the conversation means to those involved in it. Make the most of the opportunity by showing interest, asking open-ended questions and encouraging the teller to continue the story.

In hospitals, nursing or residential homes and day centres there are many opportunities to use spontaneous reminiscence. You do not always have to be 'sitting comfortably' to reminisce. Often you may be bathing someone, making their bed, tidying their bedroom, helping them to dress or to eat and the opportunity arises naturally to reminisce.

In addition to casual spontaneous openings, you may decide you want to do planned or prompted reminiscence work with an individual. If so, you should explain what you have in mind and 'contract' with the person to get their agreement. They should have a genuine choice about participating.

Individual work needs careful preparation. All the same questions about why, when, where and how need to be considered. Individual work, just as group work, may also be either 'specific' or 'general' depending on the objectives which have been agreed with the participant.

A common worry of workers concerns the beginning phase. How can you get shy, reticent people to start reminiscing? A number of techniques may help you begin.

One way to start might be to suggest you accompany the person on an imaginary walk down the street where they lived. Get them to describe what they see, telling you about both the place and its people. They may like to draw a plan or diagram by visualising the street and naming the various buildings.

This idea can be developed by asking them to think of the house in which they lived as a child and begin to walk in their imagination through each of the rooms, telling you what is in each one. People can be asked to imagine the shelf in their kitchen, garage or greenhouse and then to talk about what was kept there and what the different things were used for.

Depending on their interests, they could be asked about friends at school, members of a sports club or team, mates at work or members of their family.

Some people respond to the suggestion that they should imagine their life as if it were a garden, a house or a party and then to fill in the details from their own personal recollections.

The relationship you make with any individual person is the important thing. This grows out of shared work, a journey you take together. It is based on mutual respect. Warmth, concern and genuineness are the ingredients required if people are to entrust you with their life story.

Many of the suggestions about using triggers in groups can be applied to work with individuals. You need to consider the objectives, relevance and appropriateness of what you are planning. Pictures, particularly if they are enlarged, are very useful but do not forget other multi-sensory triggers, especially things that can be touched and handled.

Be alert to using a person's own triggers. This is obviously easier if they are living at home, when all kinds of mementoes will be available. If they are living away from home, you may need to ask relatives and friends to locate triggers. Follow the interests and preoccupations of the person, trying hard to obtain triggers that relate closely to their known life experience.

Think carefully about whether you want to contract about making a record. Explain some of the different ways this could be done. Individual work may consist only of talking together. Sometimes it may be very natural to suggest that a permanent record is made of these conversations. Never impose this on a reluctant person. At the same time, be sensitive to any tendency for them to devalue their experience, dismissing their life story as being of no interest to anyone else, and therefore not worth preserving. If a permanent record, no matter how modest, is produced, it may be kept only as a personal document or be shared with others. Either way it can be of immense value to its owner. If shared, it becomes an effective tool for communication. Various formats for making and displaying records are described later in this chapter.

Life review, reminiscence and autobiographical writing

There are many different ways of doing specific work with individuals. Only some will be mentioned while similarities and differences between life review, reminiscence and guided autobiographical writing will be described.

Life review

Life review is the kind of reminiscence that has a large element of stock-taking or self-evaluation, of coming to terms with life, of struggling to achieve integrity rather than despair. Butler (1995) stressed this aspect:

'By reviewing the past events of their lives, old people put their lives in perspective, prove to themselves that their lives have been worthwhile and prepare themselves for death with a minimum of fear or anxiety. People get much more out of the opportunity to express their thoughts and feelings to someone willing to listen. In this way they can reflect upon their lives with the intent of resolving, reorganising, and reintegrating what is troubling or preoccupying them.'

It is generally accepted that 'putting one's life in order is most intense in old age' although life reviews can be triggered spontaneously when people of any age are faced with events or crises which confront them with questions about their own identity and the meaning they attach to life.

Thinking, remembering, talking and writing are all kinds of social interaction with oneself, even if no audience is involved. Having an audience, however, either as listener, reader or viewer does appear to help to develop a 'good story'. This means a story that makes sense of life's experience and represents it in a way which the teller can live with. This introduces a social element into the individual's effort to produce a coherent story, a consistent account. The older person is not just concerned with working through the final stage of life, but actually interpreting or making sense of their whole journey to themselves and others. Tarman (1988) suggested we reminisce to make ourselves more acceptable to ourselves and more interesting to other people.

Although some writers still use the term 'life review' loosely to refer to aspects of reminiscence which contain an evaluative element, it is increasingly being used in a stricter more technical sense. Haight (1998), a nursing educator and researcher, defines it as:

> 'A short-term therapy structured reminiscing intervention conducted on a one-to-one basis with an older person. The person who conducts the process acts as a therapeutic listener who guides the older individual in his/her memories, and helps that individual to reframe troubled events and to move on in their thinking.'

Life review, reminiscence and guided autobiographical writing have both common and different characteristics.

Life review is:

- undertaken with individuals and used selectively with people with dementia;
- a planned purposeful intervention to which the person consents;
- a structured process based on a tested research-based format;
- evaluative in emphasis – the meanings or interpretations attributed to the events recounted are more important than the events themselves;
- therapeutic in intention – to help the person come to terms with his or her life;
- time-limited with a set number of sessions, usually eight, undertaken in private;
- designed to cover the whole life-span from birth to the present;
- structured so as to be a chronological or a thematic account.

The life review worker:

- guides the person to consider questions concerned with death, grief, fear, religion, school, hardships, sex, work and relationships;
- assists the person to analyse troubled events, to achieve their integration and to move on;
- uses reflective counselling skills and for this limited time becomes a confidante;

- may use the Life Review and Experience Form (LREF) to guide the interview;
- produces a tangible taped, written or visual record – a life story book;
- may undertake a parallel but separate review with a spouse or partner in private.

Reminiscence

Reminiscence may be undertaken with either individuals or small groups and:

- can be used with people either with or without dementia;
- although planned, it does not necessarily systematically cover the whole life-span;
- may explore a particular time, period, event, theme or topic;
- frequently utilises multi-sensory triggers to promote recall;
- is not deliberately therapeutic in intention – but may turn out to be;
- is not necessarily evaluative or integrative, although aspects of the process may be;
- fulfils various personal, social and cultural functions;
- may be limited to a fixed number of sessions or be open-ended;
- content is not usually tightly structured or systematic;
- the worker acts as an enabler or facilitator, not as a counsellor;
- is responsive and reactive and does explore feelings and meanings to some extent;
- uses various creative means to record and present tangible outcomes of the process;
- spouse, partner or other people may share in the reminiscence process.

Guided autobiographical writing

This approach was developed by Birren and Birren (1996). It is included in this chapter because it is a type of structured individual life review. It combines recall and reflection of memories in private with mutual group support as a means of promoting acceptance of self, insight and development.

With guided autobiographical writing:

- individuals attend ten weekly small group meetings;
- in between sessions, at home each person prepares a short written story about nine aspects of their lives;
- group members then read and discuss their writing in the group;
- group members provide feedback, support and confirmation that life has been worthwhile;
- it has a sound research base.

The nine aspects covered are:

- history of the major branching points in life;
- family history;
- career or major lifework;
- the role of money in life;
- health and body image;
- loves and hates;
- sexual identity, sexual roles and experience;
- experiences with and ideas about death, dying and other losses;
- influences, beliefs and values that provide meaning in life.

Birren and Birren (1996) quote the following positive outcomes of studies using this method:

- sense of increased personal power and importance;
- recognition of past problem-solving strategies and their application to current needs and problems;
- reconciliation with the past and resolution of past resentments and negative feelings;
- resurgence of interest in past activities or hobbies;
- development of friendships with other group members;
- greater sense of meaning in life;
- ability to face the nearing end of life with a feeling that one has contributed to the world.

There are many other imaginative ways of addressing these and related themes with individuals or small groups by means of a combination of individual work and groupwork. For example, Jan-Eric Ruth (1996), working with an artist, encouraged older people to paint or draw their lives.

By using uncomplicated drawings and diagrams, people can present important elements of their stories. Spontaneous or rehearsed drama, mime, dance and music can involve older people actively re-presenting, reworking, re-integrating and reconstructing aspects of their life experience. Frequently poetry and creative writing groups have a distinctly biographical dimension to the writing produced.

Behaviours which challenge carers

There are some older people whom staff and family members find particularly difficult. They may be excessively demanding and hard to please, noisy, aggressive, hostile, uncooperative and unhappy. Others may be equally challenging because they remain aloof, isolated and either unwilling or unable to join in the life around them. Remember that all behaviour has a purpose, even if the purpose may be hard to understand.

Frequently, staff label residents. They 'give a dog a bad name' and then are surprised that the person behaves in exactly the ways forecasted. Try to pay particular attention to troubling and troubled people. Observe them closely, spend time with them, learn about their life history. Consider whether it could be possible that the way you and other staff treat them is, in some way at least, responsible for the difficult behaviour.

The more you know about a person's past, the more likely you are to understand why they are as they are in the present. This means that you must take time to listen, to discover, probably from various sources, about the past and then to use your understanding to reach the person in the present. Work hard to create situations where the person truly feels 'heard' and respected as a unique individual.

Some people may have been very badly hurt, whether in the far distant past or the more recent past. They may be reluctant to talk. It may take time for them to trust you. Some probably never will. A key worker system in residential and nursing homes makes it more likely for warm, trusting, caring relationships to blossom.

Many routines encourage difficult behaviour because they serve the purposes of the staff more than the needs of the residents; they are not person-centred. Some routines are so long-established that no one actually knows why certain things are done in certain ways, other than that they always have been!

Try to discover whether behaviour which you find difficult is caused by the routines staff impose, or whether it springs from past pain or unmet present personal needs. A careful assessment will help you decide on possible solutions. These will need to be put into practice on a trial basis because you may never fully unravel the causes of the behaviour. Both personal and environmental factors which interact with each other may need to be changed. Being in care is a sort of bereavement, an awful painful loss, and the resulting grieving can be very difficult both for the older person and for others around them. Being in care may also revive memories of past loss and grief, emotions which are then re-experienced in the present.

Watt and Wong (1990) suggested that a few people tell the same story over and over again. It is very hard not to lose patience with them. This 'obsessive' reminiscence seems to offer little satisfaction to either teller or hearer. It becomes a recitation of negative experience which the person seems neither able to accept nor to forget. Reminiscence is not helpful to such people if they are unable, after a time, to move on from dwelling on such memories.

Generally, however, whenever you start listening to older people telling their story, you need to be prepared to follow wherever they want to take you. You need to be open to hearing, reading, respecting and responding to both the factual and the emotional content.

Care assistant 'It was as well that I was there when Tom Jones started to talk about his time as an air raid warden and how he had not been able to get a child out of a building. I listened very carefully and I then asked him about other times and he was able to tell me how he had helped bring out a whole family in a later raid. I do think it helped him not to get stuck just on what he had not been able to do. I helped him see the other side of things as well and not to blame himself as much as when he first began.'

Methods used for recording and presenting reminiscence and life story work

Many of the approaches described briefly below provide rich possibilities for involving family members as active participants and contributors. The process itself, as much as the outcomes may enliven caring and enrich relationships. It is well to remember that while involving family members in reminiscence work can be mutually enjoyable and rewarding, some may discover, perhaps for the first time, aspects of their family history they find shocking or disturbing. Develop your own ideas about how best to undertake and present life story work.

Life story books The idea of life story books or 'This Is Your Life' type scrapbooks has been adapted from child care work. Some residential and nursing homes ask new residents to bring with them such a record in order to help staff begin to make relationships and to help the newcomer settle in. Others make the construction of a life story book an integral part of their relationship-building work with each resident.

Life story books take many forms. There is no standard way of either preparing or presenting them. Some may be very simple, others more elaborate. It is best to compile them in a way that makes it easy for alterations or additions to be made. Some form of loose-leaf binder to which extra sheets and plastic pockets can be added is probably best. Loose-leaf, stick-down cellophane photograph album sheets can also be used. It then becomes relatively simple to preserve personal writing, tape transcriptions, photographs, significant personal documents such as school reports, birth, death and marriage certificates, invitations, letters, personal papers, newspaper cuttings and pictures, and other materials about the person and the period and places in which they have lived. Issues of ownership, access, consent and confidentiality are very important and must be negotiated with each person who is asked to work on creating such a record.

A life story book should be thought of as a 'living' working document, subject to change, modification and expansion. The process of preparing it can be as important as the final outcome. It is a record of the past as well as a record for the present. It can be updated from time to time but the story is never fully told. Even after a person dies, he or she lives on in the lives of others whom they have known, in their memories and stories.

Photograph albums with or without explanatory notes, can be a way of constructing a life story book. Usually the photographs are arranged in chronological order over all or chronologically within themes. Some minimal identification increases the usefulness of the collection.

Family trees may form part of a life story book or they may be used as another means of tracing, recording and 'placing' the older person. There are now computer programs for compiling family trees but they are not hard to draw by hand. These may possibly be enlarged and displayed in people's rooms. Do take care because people may have unconventional family trees which they may find difficult to complete and may not wish to display in public. Always seek agreement for what is proposed, and do not proceed without it. Life maps and network diagrams are pictorial representations with brief text added of significant events and people.

Time lines or life lines help stimulate recall and help both teller and listener to keep track of what is being told. They are a simple way of recording major milestones and significant life events. It is easy to add to the personal record, if people wish to do so, a parallel time line that shows major national or international events which helps place the personal history within a public perspective, and vice versa.

Memory boxes developed by the European Reminiscence Network, originally using obsolete army ammunition boxes, enable a three-dimensional representation of a person's life to be made. Photographs, documents, personal memorabilia and cherished artefacts are included. Such boxes have great potential for involving other family members or younger people in inter-generational projects. They can be constructed in group sessions where conversation about the contents and their significance is as important as their arrangement in the box.

Lifescapes are a similar idea to memory boxes, where a framed visual presentation of significant memorabilia is constructed. Wall hangings, collages, mosaics and murals containing visual representations of aspects of a person's life, or the collective lives of members of a group are also used.

Story boards are usually enriched with photographs, and summarise the outcome of planned reminiscence sessions. They have been used in residential and hospital settings and for people going into short-term respite care. They have great potential in domiciliary care work. Day centres or workshops could possibly assist in the preparation of the boards to be used by reminiscence workers or volunteers. They could then be displayed in people's own homes where they would be both a tangible reminder of the lived experience and a focus for conversation with professional carers, family carers and visitors. Less elaborate scrap books or annotated photograph albums can be used in similar ways.

Tape recordings

Audio recording is becoming increasingly popular in both group and individual work. It is much easier to make a good quality audio recording of an individual than of a group. Audio recordings can be more useful if a transcription is made. This is a time-consuming task, but it enables you to analyse and reflect upon your skills in working with individuals and groups. Sections within tapes can then be easily identified for replaying and using as triggers in future. Even with a full transcription, an index or summary is very helpful. Usually a cassette copy is given to people who record their life stories.

Tape recorders are easy to use and most people quickly accept them. Experience shows that only a few people are put off by them beyond the first few minutes. Sound tape deteriorates over time unless kept in an even temperature. If you intend taping an interview, you need to have a clear agreement before you begin about who owns the record, how and when it may be used and where it is to be kept. Any reservations about access must be respected.

Read a guide to tape recorders and tape recording before starting. A number are available (see page 91). Either poor machinery or poor recording techniques produce unusable recordings. Many of the pitfalls can be readily overcome with some simple instruction and practice.

Because some libraries, local radio stations, museums with sound archives and local history societies are so interested in obtaining oral recordings, they will often lend or hire tape recorders. In return, tapes will be stored in proper archival conditions, preventing deterioration, and the donor will be given a cassette copy.

Some points on making sound recordings:

- use as good a machine as you can afford, preferably one with a noise reduction system;
- use an external microphone rather than relying on the in-built one;
- use new C60 or C90 cassettes, not C120s – the shorter tapes are more robust;
- choose a quiet place without background noise, preferably a room with soft furnishings;
- learn to work the recorder before you begin;
- check and adjust sound and volume levels;
- place the recorder within approximately 18–24 inches of the person. Better still, use a lapel microphone when recording individuals. Group recordings require a different kind of microphone;
- if using a microphone on a stand, do not place it on the same surface as the recorder;
- plan beforehand what you intend to ask. Have a list of prepared questions to use as a guide;
- learn to ask only one question at a time and do not interrupt the response;
- ask different kinds of questions including open or descriptive, specific or factual, feeling and expansive types of questions;
- write identifying details giving name, location and date on the cassette and on its box;
- keep an index of topics or a summary written as soon as possible after the interview.

Video recording

Be very cautious before embarking on reminiscence film-making. It is very time-consuming and very difficult to do well. To be filmed is much more intimidating than to be recorded on sound tape. Video technology is very intrusive, lighting and sound may be problematic and the final product, unless made by very experienced people, is usually not worth the effort. Everyone is so accustomed to high-quality television that poor-quality amateur video film gives little pleasure or satisfaction.

A video shot of a person talking to the camera or to an interviewer for more than a few minutes usually becomes very boring. To film in different locations requires great organisation, effort, skill and usually a number of helpers. Film of activities, for example a person demonstrating a craft, game or skill is more interesting than conversation without action.

Sometimes it may be possible to involve media studies students from local colleges, but if you use media people you risk losing control. They will have their own exacting standards, and your objectives and theirs may be hard to reconcile.

Using computers to write life stories

The Eurolink Age New Technology Network (1996) is promoting the development of opportunities for older people to acquire computer skills and access to new technology. The 'New Tricks' project at the University of Ulster and work by other members of the Network has clearly demonstrated the value of older people using information technology to write and produce their life stories. Some of this writing is being shared across national and generational boundaries by older people's use of e-mail.

The widely-held view which suggests that older people are unable to master, and are not interested in modern technology is neither true nor acceptable. Provided older learners have access to support as they learn and are highly motivated to work on a task that is important to them, such as writing their family history or their life story, they can master word processing and other computing functions, even though it may take them longer to learn than younger people.

Open and distance computer learning materials are available from the National Extension College (see Appendix 3). Public libraries are increasingly providing bookable open access computing facilities.

When introducing older learners to computers, the following guidelines are important:

- a relaxed, informal teaching style is necessary to allay computer anxiety;
- much encouragement and reassurance is necessary, especially in the early stages, until confidence is established;
- computers need to be demystified and technical language used very sparingly and only in response to students' questions;
- being in a class with younger people is uncomfortable until basic computer competence has been achieved. Mixed age groups are then more acceptable;
- in the early stage of learning, twice-weekly sessions are recommended;
- ready access to a computer for additional practice in between sessions is helpful;
- open learning manuals or notes enable each student to work at their own pace;
- a non-competitive, cooperative learning environment encourages older students;
- motivation is increased by early and frequent evidence of achievement in the form of hard copy;
- informal assistance from older mentors is most acceptable and much appreciated.

Teaching older people to be responsible for their own writing and its production in an attractive format using desktop publishing has limitless possibilities. Acquiring computer skills and using them to accomplish reminiscence and life history work, or other tasks of personal significance can be genuinely empowering.

Some people are content to write for their own private consumption, many write for their families. Others are driven by a desire to publish. Remember that writing is a complex process. Present circumstances, the passage of time, the intensity of emotion associated with the original memories and their recall, the effects of rehearsal, and the need to adapt the recalled memories so they fit with the writer's present ideas about themselves and how they wish to be perceived by others will all have an influence.

What people record, write and make public encourages others to begin to write. Sharing, through reading aloud their own writings, can be an enormously enriching, emotionally moving experience. It values people's lives and acknowledges the effort that has been expended in making the record.

Some ethical considerations

Reminiscence workers, like oral historians, face the dilemma of whether or not it is acceptable to talk with older people for the express purpose of recording their recollections, then, once done, abandoning them. There is no simple answer to this dilemma which must be addressed afresh in each particular situation. Valerie Yow (1994), an oral historian, has written with great clarity about such ethical concerns.

The essential guiding principle is to be open, honest and explicit about the purpose of any contact, the nature and likely duration of the relationship, and possible outcomes from the beginning. Most older people can accept time limits and time-limited relationships, painful as the ending may be. What they should not be asked to accept is being misled, used and then abandoned.

In all such work, the process of engagement needs to be conducted ethically. So too does the nature and management of any tangible outcomes which may also implicate other people who feature in the stories. You need to be aware of and to take responsibility for the ethical ramifications of your reminiscence work and to try in every possible way to achieve informed consent on the part of all participants. This consent needs to include an agreement about the nature of any tangible outcome, where it will be kept and who may have access to it.

KEY POINTS

■ The interaction of life history and present circumstances influences troubling present behaviour.

■ Many individuals and their families are enriched both by the process of making a tangible life history record and the record itself.

■ The record can be presented in various formats depending on the objectives to be served, and the interests, energy, expertise and resources available.

■ The 'product' belongs to the person. Their ownership must be respected.

■ Both the means and ends, the process and the outcomes must be informed by ethical behaviour.

APPLICATION EXERCISES

1 Write down five key words that relate to this chapter. Now write down why these words are important to your work with individuals.

2 What more do you need to learn about or follow up as a result of having read this chapter?

3 Assist someone in making a record of their own life story.

Further Reading

Older People and New Technology. Second European Network Meeting Report and Directory (June 1996) by Eurolink Age, London, 1996.

Oral History: Talking about the past by R Perks. Historical Association/Oral History Society, London, 1995.

The Oral History Reader by R Perks and A Thomson. Routledge, London, 1998.

7 Reminiscence with Ethnic Minority Elders

This chapter includes:

- Cultural differences towards ageing, death and dying
- Growing old in a second homeland
- The importance of bearing witness
- Black and white co-working
- Inter-generational and cross-cultural reminiscence work

To do effective reminiscence work with people from ethnic minority groups it is important to learn about their history, religion, values, beliefs, customs and traditions. Broad general knowledge can only provide a background for there are innumerable differences both within groups and between groups. It is also necessary to know something about British colonial history, and Twentieth Century immigration and asylum policies. Getting to know individual people from backgrounds which differ from your own will help prevent stereotyping. It will help you appreciate each person as a unique individual, not just as a member of a group to which you ascribe general characteristics. This cuts both ways. As you respect other people as individuals, so too do you have a right to expect that they will respect you as an individual.

As with all effective reminiscence work, respect for people, regardless of age, race, culture, religion, politics, gender, and sexual orientation, is essential. Discriminatory attitudes and behaviour are unacceptable, and sensitive anti-discriminatory practice will be necessary if racism, or any other form of discrimination, surfaces in a reminiscence group.

Differences towards ageing, death and dying

Being invited to tell one's story is likely to evoke different responses in people from different ethnic backgrounds. For some it may be a natural thing to do, for others it may seem a strange invitation. There may also be class, caste, gender and educational differences, so do not expect everyone to respond in the same way.

If people share a common heritage, common origins, language and values, groupwork is likely to be more spontaneous than it might otherwise be. People from the same background will probably enjoy reminiscing with each other but reminiscence work in a group of people from different ethnic backgrounds is possible and, in some care situations, very desirable.

Reminiscence work as outlined in this book, with its emphasis on personal life history, albeit shared with others, may seem strangely western and therefore irrelevant to older people from some other traditions. Not for everyone does the life lived give meaning to old age. Respect for elders and valuing the wisdom they have attained will be very important in some societies, but not in all. You will need to consider very carefully the culture and traditions of the people you wish to work with, and adapt your reminiscence work accordingly.

For example, some white British and Asian older people approach old age and death differently. They do not view life satisfaction in the same way. You must not expect everyone to believe or accept western ideas. For example, many westerners believe that there is one, and only one life. Followers of some other world religions believe there will be many previous and future lives.

You also need to appreciate that other cultures have different views about how much people as they age should remain involved in everyday life. Contemplation rather than active engagement in late life may be preferred in some cultures.

In some eastern religions a sense of personal fulfilment and absence of fear about the future, especially fear of death, is more public, less of a private and a personal affair than in the west. Older people from non-Christian backgrounds may find an emphasis on personal recollection and individual life history very odd, very self-centred. They may have a greater sense of community, of being connected to others, and reminiscence work needs to reflect these varied traditions.

Growing old in a second homeland

The life story connects each of us to our 'place' and our own culture. If these connections have been disrupted for whatever reason, perhaps because of war, becoming a refugee, emigration, or separation from home or family it is particularly important to help people reconnect with their past and to remember significant relationships and familiar places.

Most of us who experience loss of significant places, in whatever circumstances, for whatever reasons, feel a kind of grief, or what Peter Read (1996) calls 'bereavement of place.' Our own awareness of lost places, near or far, of being 'strangers' in unfamiliar circumstances may help us to appreciate, to some extent, the sense of loss, anxiety, and dislocation experienced by others.

Growing old in a second homeland, or growing old as a member of an ethnic minority group, even if born in Britain, may mean being disadvantaged in many different ways. People from all backgrounds who are healthy, well housed and economically secure do best in later life. Many immigrants and asylum seekers may experience poor health, poor housing and have had a long history of poorly paid employment or unemployment which results in dependence on inadequate state benefits in old age. Many do not manage to get adequate help from the health and social services. They may well feel insecure, isolated and be poorly provided for in late life. Having lost a homeland, they may not have gained a secure, respected place in their country of adoption.

Group reminiscence for people from ethnic minorities may therefore be an important way of linking them back into their own communities and reaffirming their own cultural traditions. If managed sensitively, such work may help to convey a sense of respect, warmth and genuine interest in cultural diversity. It can help confirm both common and different characteristics and help people to value their life experience and cultural heritage. If workers are insensitive or treat people in ways experienced or perceived as disrespectful, the older person from a different background will feel hurt, isolated and demeaned.

As a care worker you may have some difficulty in empathising with the feelings of people who have grown old in a second homeland, especially if you are young and have not experienced immigration first hand. On the other hand, you too may belong to an ethnic minority group, even if born in Britain. Whatever our own origins and life experience, we all need to be open to learning about 'difference' and to appreciate how we feel and behave towards people who are 'different' from ourselves.

Many immigrants and refugees regard their new country with mixed feelings. Some may be proud and well satisfied. For some who may have experienced economic hardship, ill health, racism and loneliness, living in Britain may have been an unhappy, unrewarding experience, now made worse by lack of adequate care in old age.

Some 'new comers' may feel they have failed and experience a deep, probably unattainable, longing to return to their homeland. Many realise the place they have left will no longer be the same, even if they could afford to return. Difficulties overcome, personal success and family success should also be applauded. Scarcely for anyone will life have been entirely negative. Reminiscence work uncovers pain but also provides many openings for affirmation, encouragement and recognition of courage and achievement.

Immigration is not inevitably experienced as loss and it will seldom be seen as totally negative. It will be a mixture of pain and pleasure, loss and gain, relinquishment, and new beginnings. There are likely to be very mixed feelings about leaving home, immigration, settling and now growing old in a foreign land. Therefore it is essential for you to be finely tuned to the older person in the here and now; to understand what their present, as well as past concerns are; and to be willing to share that experience, at the pace and in the ways in which the person wishes to recount it.

It is vitally important that you take the time and trouble to learn about different ethnic groups as well as to understand about the personal life experience of any particular individual. One effective way of gaining this knowledge is to listen attentively to ethnic elders – older people from ethnic minority communities – talking about their own homelands. Ask them questions, read, try to appreciate what life used to be like for them and in what ways it may have changed.

Much of the fine detail of their stories will be affected by each individual's present circumstances and how receptive he or she perceives the audience to be. Careful selection of triggers will be necessary so that they represent the homeland as well as the new land. Families, community groups, churches and mosques, local ethnic radio stations, embassies, consulates, museums and libraries may be able to assist in locating culturally relevant triggers.

The same guidelines about group membership, good communication and building relationships already mentioned apply to work with same-race and mixed-race groups as well as to individual work. If the leaders of a multi-racial group share the same background as members, difficulties of communication and language will obviously be lessened. If you are a 'stranger', this is an opportunity for the older people to become your teacher in a very real sense.

Ethnic elders are likely to be a very small minority in most day centres, nursing homes, hospitals and residential homes. Nevertheless, even if small in numbers, their different needs for communication, information, food, hygiene, hair care, religious observance, funerals and mourning customs need sensitive attention.

Religious festivals such as Eid-ul-Fitr, Eid-ul-Adha (Moslem), Diwali, Holi (Hindu), and Passover, Hanukkah (Jewish) can provide opportunities for reminiscence about past celebrations in distant places as well as being opportunities for valuing a person's special identity and extending others' understanding. Celebrations using music, song, dance and food may be organised around important national Caribbean independence dates, Chinese New Year, St Patrick's Day, St David's Day, St Andrew's Day and other special occasions.

Cultural continuity achieved through teaching and passing on traditions to inform and influence the next generation is very important in many reminiscence projects with people from ethnic minority groups. Reminiscence can also help with linking the past with the present, in problem-solving, relationship-building and coming to terms with life as it has turned out.

Reminiscence as problem-solving may be especially relevant to older people who live in residential homes or nursing homes that are not finely tuned to their cultural, dietary and religious needs and interests. It could become a constructive, helpful means for drawing attention to different traditions and for influencing carers to respond more appropriately to their needs.

Day Centre Co-ordinator for the League of Jewish Women 'Often past lives were talked about for the first time in our reminiscence group. Non-Jewish staff could join in and make comparisons with their own past and tell of their own religious traditions. Probably the most important spin-off was the opportunity it gave to care staff and social workers to understand more about the different world their residents and clients had come from.'

Reminiscence as life review may be too painful for some, but helpful for those who can accept their past experience, its joys and disappointments. They may have experienced enormous loss and change, and it may take immigrants or refugees longer to trust themselves to talk about their deepest concerns. Some may not wish to share their life review, for them a private process, particularly if they have had a hard struggle to come to terms with life's events. Some may feel caught in a struggle to live life in two places, of wanting desperately to hang on to their old traditions while needing to accommodate to present circumstances.

The importance of bearing witness

Many immigrants and refugees have an overwhelming urge to 'bear witness'. For some, their pain has been so terrible, their loss so great that it takes them many years to be able to face the enormity of their suffering. This has been seen most vividly in Jewish survivors of the Nazi Holocaust, but with continued wars in many parts of the world, similar reactions in newer refugees of many nationalities can be anticipated.

Some may find that no amount of telling can remove their suffering, while others are quite unable to break their silence and to speak of the unspeakable. The questions 'Why was I spared?', 'How could it happen?' may become a preoccupation in later life when more time for looking back and for reflection is available.

Reminiscence in inter-generational family groups is particularly relevant, although often very complex, as shown by Dan Bar-On (1995), who undertook family history work across three generations in families where the grandparents were survivors of the Holocaust and other wartime suffering. Putting the record straight, telling it as it was by at last breaking the silence is one way of honouring the dead, validating the experience, justifying the survival of the witness. Such work is very demanding and requires great skill.

Some writers have suggested that people who have endured terrible suffering or extreme trauma are sometimes unable to speak about it to their children but eventually, long after the event, are able to do so with their grandchildren. The book by Hunt, Marshall and Rowlings (see page 160) contains case examples of people who in earlier life experienced different kinds of trauma which only emerged or, for some people, re-emerged in late life. There is still much to learn about the timing and the context in which life stories come to be told.

Black and white co-working

White reminiscence workers may unknowingly be perceived as dominating, condescending or oppressive, so they must take particular care to be well informed, sensitive and open.

> **Care worker** 'We need to be aware of our own feelings. We need to be honest about how we feel about older people generally and race in particular if we are to ease some of the hurt.'

The experience of all immigrants will not be the same, even though they all share the common elements of leaving, journeying, arriving, settling and the feeling of never completely belonging. To be old in Britain and to be Irish, Polish, Chinese, Asian, African or Caribbean will not be the same experience. Do not assume that reminiscing with one minority group will be any easier than reminiscing with another, just because you share a common first language. Shared language obviously helps but many other subtle factors are also important.

Reminiscence groups that touch on the harsh realities of discrimination may be hard for white leaders and members to cope with because their own racial attitudes and national identity will be challenged. Accounts of racism and discrimination at work or school, abuse, violence, being refused accommodation and denied employment, educational opportunities or care which others take for granted, are liable to arouse guilt, defensiveness or denial. Both tellers and hearers will be touched in many different ways. Effective groupwork demands that feelings, no matter how painful and threatening, be openly talked about and honestly acknowledged.

Take particular care to overcome any language barriers in order to make it possible for people to participate in reminiscence work. Invitations and notices may need to be written in various languages depending on who is to be invited. The most common languages and dialects encountered will probably be Punjabi, Hindi, Urdu, Gujerati, Kutchi, Bengali, Sylheti, Cantonese, Mandarin and patois.

Consider using interpreters. When looking for assistance with interpretation, begin within your own workplace. Are there any staff members who speak the required language who could be asked to help? If not, look elsewhere. Some local authorities provide an interpreter service. Many social services fieldwork teams have social workers from varied ethnic backgrounds. Local community groups and language agencies may be pleased to become involved as volunteers. Local schools may be delighted to work with you to open up opportunities for community service by their pupils and staff.

Any co-working relationship is complex, as has already been explained in Chapter 4. Black and white co-working in groups is even more complex. It is another factor to be considered at the planning stage. What should be the mix of age, class and gender? Should the group and its leaders be all black, all white or mixed black and white? Some people, both black and white, question whether black/white co-working is ever possible or acceptable. It is important for you to know where you stand on such issues so you are not caught out unawares when becoming involved in reminiscence groupwork. Mistry and Brown (1991), social work teachers, suggest that: 'black/white co-worker pairing is usually desirable where the group is racially mixed and there are potential benefits associated with joint working.'

Co-working requires consideration of the following:

- Are you willing and able to model co-leadership?
- Have you agreed general ground rules?
- Decide how many workers to have. Should it be one, two or more?
- Is a black/white pair appropriate?
- Can you work comfortably with the particular person proposed?
- Do you agree over purpose, principles and practice?
- Can you talk openly about the race dimension of the partnership?
- Have you talked about issues of authority between yourselves and within the group?
- Have you agreed how racism will be handled in the group?
- Have you agreed how differences in background, aptitudes, skill, experience and ability are to be handled between the co-workers?
- Have you planned to share tasks on a fifty/fifty basis so that the white worker will not automatically be cast as the leader?
- Are you able to give each other feedback on performance? Can you be honest with each other?
- Have you agreed about supervision and consultation?

Inter-generational and/or cross-cultural reminiscence work

Inter-generational work can be very rewarding for both younger and older people when undertaken in either same-race groups or mixed-race groups. The value of inter-generational projects is not limited to preserving and passing on skills and memories of people from ethnic minority groups, although the very rich potential for doing so may be more immediately apparent within these groups.

Children of all ages and students in all kinds of schools and colleges can benefit in many different ways from working directly with older people. Inter-generational projects utilising older people as living resources, models and mentors are growing in popularity. Many projects link local schools with hospitals, homes, day centres and community groups. Older people comment very favourably about their participation in projects which break down age barriers.

Inter-generational work takes many different forms and brings mutual social as well as educational benefits. Older people are able to share their knowledge of varied life experience, history, geography and other subjects with younger people who appreciate hearing vivid first-hand accounts of past times. Careful preparation of both the older and younger participants in any project is essential. Relationships take time to develop, children and older people need help in preparing the topics to be covered during the visits, and follow-up work by the children, if shared with the older informants, brings mutual pleasure and satisfaction.

> **Volunteer school reminiscence worker** 'We show them what they cannot get from books. Nobody can get it from a book, what we know. The day I go to school is the best day of my week.'

Often projects begin with very modest objectives, but as people begin to enjoy their involvement, ideas develop and valued relationships, new knowledge, activities and products emerge. Plays, musicals, exhibitions, events, outings, visits, entertainments, published stories, books and poems as well as conventional and e-mail correspondence, friendship, increased understanding and mutual respect have all developed out of inter-generational work.

Liz Bartlett (1992), Co-ordinator of the Kensington and Chelsea Community History Group illustrates the dynamic nature of such work in her account of a lunch club for Afro-Caribbean community elders:

> 'The topic – food – in one reminiscence session developed over time into a book with the title *Nice Tastin': Life and Food in the Caribbean*. Members of the club went in every week to two classes in a nearby primary school, where they passed on some of their knowledge of the culture. The children responded by producing wonderful drawings of Caribbean fruits and vegetables, they learnt how to cook potato pone, and they especially enjoyed story-reading and storytelling sessions.'

Conclusion

The courage, resilience and strength of older people, especially those from minority cultures, need to be recognised and celebrated. Reminiscence as witnessing, teaching, problem-solving and stock-taking is important. It connects the person to their culture, both past and present. People whose lives have been disrupted by geographic dispersal, emigration and separation from home and family may find it particularly helpful. Some of this experience may be mirrored in late life (and possibly reactivated for some) by the pain of divorce, bereavement, or admission to care. Reconnecting through reminiscence and recall to important past events, significant relationships, and special places may make the present more agreeable or at least more tolerable.

Ethnically sensitive reminiscence work will not solve the problems of inequality. It is, however, a way of challenging discrimination, extending mutual understanding and establishing warm, respectful, caring relationships. This will not happen automatically, but only as we confront our own prejudice and become open to learning from people whose race, beliefs, language and life experience differ from our own. Small reminiscence groups and individual life story work offer a sympathetic climate in which this process might begin.

KEY POINTS

■ Be alert to the possibility that you may be imposing your own culture and values on others.

■ Develop your understanding about what it is like to grow old in a second homeland through reading, sensitive questioning and careful listening.

■ Ethnically sensitive reminiscence work can help to inform about differences of religion, ethnicity, age, gender, class and status.

■ Cross-cultural groups can share common life experiences if not a shared cultural inheritance.

■ Inter-generational and cross-cultural work can be rewarding for both older and younger people.

APPLICATION EXERCISES

1 Find an older person whose ethnic origins differ from your own. Ask if he or she will teach you about the important aspects of their own culture, especially attitudes and practices concerned with family life, age and ageing, death and dying.

2 Begin to develop a co-working relationship with a colleague whose ethnic background differs from your own. Try reading and then discussing together this chapter before commencing joint reminiscence work.

3 When planning reminiscence work with an older person(s) from a minority group, locate some relevant multi-sensory triggers which take account of age, gender, geography and culture.

Further Reading

Age Exchanges: Reminiscence projects for children and older people by P Schweitzer. Age Exchange, London, 1993.

Caring for Ethnic Minority Elders: A guide by Y Alibhai-Brown. Age Concern Books, London, 1998.

Making Memories Matter: Reminiscence and inter-generational activities. Papers from European Reminiscence Symposium by P Schweitzer (ed). European Reminiscence Network, London, 1995.

Race and Groupwork by T Mistry and A Brown (eds). Whiting and Birch, London, 1997.

8 Reminiscence with People with Dementia

This chapter includes:

- Some information about dementia
- Communicating with people with dementia
- Guidelines for planned reminiscence work in small groups
- Guidelines for specific prompted reminiscence with individuals
- Differences between reminiscence, reality orientation and validation therapy

Some information about dementia

Professional and family carers, friends and neighbours all find that dementia stretches our understanding, patience, perseverance and love. All too frequently professional carers' pessimism leaves people with dementia and their family carers unsupported and isolated. The challenge of dementia is to find ways of staying in touch, of continuing to communicate.

'Dementia' is an umbrella term which refers to a group of progressive organic diseases of the brain, not to a single disease, which result in a severe and progressive decline in memory, reasoning and comprehension. Dementia is not an inevitable consequence of ageing. Most, but not all dementias, however, overtake people in late life. A few people develop dementia in mid-life, or even earlier. The chances of being affected increase considerably from approximately three in every hundred people over sixty-five years of age to between ten and fifteen in every hundred people over eighty.

Definitions, diagnosis and assessment methods are not standardised and so it is difficult to calculate accurately the number of people with dementia. In the UK some 600,000 people are thought to have dementia. The numbers are growing because as more people live longer, the number with dementia will increase. Dementia appears to occur in all countries, regardless of gender, social class, income, education and ethnic group.

There is on-going debate about the causes of dementia. Although various factors are implicated in the neurological deterioration which occurs, how any one person is affected depends on a complicated mix of physical factors, life experience, psychological factors (including unresolved past trauma), social interactions and present circumstances. Alzheimer's disease is the most well known dementia and often people use this term loosely to refer to all dementias, no matter what their type or cause. Alzheimer's disease and Lewy body dementia have no known cure, the cause is uncertain, their progression variable and they probably account for well over 50 per cent of all cases. Some recently available drugs improve the symptoms in some people for a short time in the early stages of Alzheimer's disease.

Multi-infarct or vascular dementia is another common type. This is caused by repeated small strokes or haemorrhages in the brain. Preventive positive health measures throughout life and treatment for high blood pressure may help to some extent. Other dementias include those associated with Aids, CJD and excessive alcohol intake. It is possible to have more than one type of dementia simultaneously. See *Dementia Reconsidered* by Tom Kitwood (1997) for further information about dementia and a person-centred approach to dementia care.

It is important, but not always easy, to distinguish dementia and depression as some of the symptoms may resemble each other. Powell (1995), a liaison nurse, has wrtitten about disentangling the two different conditions. In dementia, the age of onset, the ways in which mental and physical health are affected, accompanying behavioural and mood changes, and the speed of deterioration vary greatly from person to person.

The term 'confusion' is often used instead of dementia. This is unhelpful because it tells us nothing about the type of dementia and its causes, the nature and speed of decline and how long the person affected may survive. Confusion is a symptom, rather than a disease. Many people with a dementing illness are indeed 'confused' about themselves, other people, where they are, and the time of day.

Except in the very advanced stages, people with dementia are seldom totally confused. They may be clear about some things and very mixed up about others. Some die early, others live for many years. Some people's behaviour may be very difficult and demanding, beyond their control. Yet there are others who, if treated in ways that respect them as unique individuals, seem able, to some extent, to behave differently.

In the early stages of dementia, as they become more and more aware of their failing memory, many people feel very anxious, agitated, restless and depressed. Other losses and changes in their life, especially losing someone very close to them, or moving to an unfamiliar environment, will make their problems noticeably worse.

As the disease develops people find it hard, but not always impossible, to learn new skills or information, to remember or to recall on demand old information, to hold a sensible conversation, and to manage personal and domestic affairs, including personal hygiene. They are unaware of danger, get lost in familiar places, unable to make decisions or to plan ahead. At times their behaviour can cause embarrassment and offence. As the disease progresses they are likely to grow more and more isolated, cut off from others, who may be slow to realise initially that something serious is wrong.

Often relatives, friends and neighbours feel that the person with dementia is just being difficult. As deterioration continues, both professional and family carers need to find ways of dealing with their own anxiety – shall I go the same way? We need to develop our capacity to continue to relate to the person with dementia as a real person, with real feelings, not just a dependent non-person needing only physical care. We have to find ways of reinforcing their humanity, rather than undermining their already precarious sense of self.

Although dementia affects all memory functions sooner or later, it is memory for recent things that is lost first. Recall of more distant times, places and people, especially memories relating to personal life experience, may remain relatively intact or partially intact far into the disease. It is possible to key into this early autobiographical memory to extract its riches, encourage conversation and preserve sociability. This is possible even if the person is unable to remember what day of the week it is, where they are or what they had for breakfast. In order to use reminiscence with people with dementia, great sensitivity, patience and skill are required.

The guidance given in earlier chapters is relevant but needs to be substantially modified for working with people with dementia. Here the important objectives are concerned with preventing further deterioration and even improving communication. Sustaining carers, developing their understanding, informing assessment, enriching relationships, reducing boredom through engagement in social activities, and preserving a sense of identity and self-esteem are the major objectives of reminiscence work in dementia care. Increasingly, workers with professional training are also using reminiscence in systematic life reviews, counselling and psychotherapy with disturbed people who have dementia.

If you want to undertake reminiscence work with people with dementia you must set yourself realistic goals, taking account of your own level of expertise, the amount of supervision available and the context in which you are working.

Caring for people with dementia can be very stressful. It is important to try to concentrate on what people can still do, rather than be overwhelmed by what they can no longer do. Too often they suffer the double jeopardy of their own 'mindlessness' (dementia means to be out of one's mind) and the 'mindlessness' of carers who in a thousand thoughtless ways set them up for failure.

Many workers are surprised at the unexpected ways in which people with dementia can join in reminiscence. Even if the response seems very small judged by 'ordinary' standards, it can be very pleasing to the older person. Their responses and their obvious pleasure can help to hold them in warm, reassuring relationships.

Communicating with people with dementia

Professional and family carers need to discover better ways of communicating which reach beyond the conventional limits of ordinary speech. Despite language and memory problems, Goldsmith (1996) argues that it is possible to communicate with people with dementia. It requires great patience, time and a willingness to try to see the world through their eyes, rather than through your own. By careful listening to conversation about the past you can learn to appreciate the person, as they used to be and as they now are. Attitudes are far more important than techniques.

Everyone, with or without dementia, uses both words and body language to communicate. When brain damage disrupts verbal language, skill in reading body or non-verbal language becomes even more important. Here are some simple tips, which are also relevant to communication with people who have other types of learning, hearing or speech difficulties:

- Check the basics. Spectacles need to be clean and of the right prescription, hearing aids functioning and dentures fitting properly.
- Eye contact is always important when you are either speaking or listening. Sit in a good light and do not cover your mouth with your hand.
- Try to be calm and to remain calm. Stay still and concentrate your attention so that you are listening attentively.
- Moving around or changing places can distract. Locating a speaker by visualising where they are helps keep track of what the person is saying.
- If a person is restless, you may want to link your arm in theirs and walk together but talking while walking may not be easy.

- Speak slowly and clearly but never in a childish way. Do not talk down to people nor talk over their heads to someone else.
- Do not compete with other distractions such as the radio or television.
- If you cannot eliminate such distractions, move to another room.
- At times it may be helpful to use touch if this seems acceptable.
- Use short sentences. If asking questions, these should be simple and direct. Ask only one question at a time.
- Try rephrasing if you are not understood, always using low, not high-pitched tones.
- Relate to the person's underlying emotions and intended communication, as you understand it, rather than insisting on factual accuracy.
- If you are hurried and tense, there is every possibility that the person with dementia will sense this.
- Use smiles and head nods. Appear relaxed – taking up a relaxed posture helps you to become relaxed.
- Laughter binds people together. Shared pleasure, even without words, brings people closer.

If you want a person with dementia to undertake a task, break it down into small steps. This way there is a better chance of them being able to perform the task. Like ourselves, the person will be pleased and encouraged by success.

Reminiscence is only one imaginative means which can be used to challenge the social isolation of older people, especially older people with dementia. Music, touch, dance, drama, art and movement can also be used, or used in conjunction with reminiscence. It must not be assumed that loss of memory automatically means loss of creativity.

Rather than thinking the seemingly garbled, often repetitive talk of people with dementia is meaningless, some people are learning to 'read', unravel and relate to the symbolism, metaphor and emotional content of the words used. John Killick (1994), a poet, listens very attentively to nursing home residents, records their conversations and then gives back to the older person their words as poetry. He explains it in this way:

'It seems to me that language used by people with dementia is a metaphorical one – where what they say often does not make sense in the usual literal way but has a poetic or symbolic meaning. People express themselves in language nearer to poetry than they used before. For example, one lady talked about her experience as a monkey puzzle, and another expressed a yearning for freedom as riding on a swing.'

Sometimes the conversation refers to the past; sometimes to poignant, insightful comment on the present. Here are two examples from his book *You Are Words: Dementia poems* (1997):

You Are Words

Life is a bit of a strain,
in view of what is to come.
Sometimes I feel embarrassed
talking to anybody, even you.
You don't really like to burden
other people with your problems.

I have been a strict person.
What people and children do now
is completely different. Any beauty
or grace has been desecrated.
The circle of life is shot away.
I want to thank you for listening.

You see, you are words.
Words can make or break you.
Sometimes people don't listen,
they give you words back,
and they're all broken, patched up.

But will you permit me to say
that you have the stillness of silence,
that listens and lasts.

Grass

A young fella carried me
in here; it were a long way
and a long time ago.
I were lying on grass ...

I don't want to stay, no
there's nothing for me
they're all very kind
but I don't want to be
inside anywhere at all
it's much too hot and bright
it just don't feel right
I've not been used

I need the fresh air
I keep calling out;
Nurse, Nurse, carry me
outside to where
I were lying on grass ...

In addition to these creative ways of reaching out to older people with dementia, designing accommodation and furnishing it in ways similar to times remembered is increasingly common in facilities offering care to older people. Mary Marshall (1998) describes internationally-accepted principles of design, and John Sumpton (1994) shows how to use familiar features. This design of the living environment may apply to an entire facility or sometimes to particular rooms which provide a sympathetic ambience in which to locate reminiscence work. Reminiscence gardens utilising old fashioned perfumed plants and safe wandering areas are also popular.

Residential care worker 'I furnished a room in Shankill House as a Belfast kitchen-house. Walking into it with a resident is like walking into their past. We have another room furnished as a pub with old fashioned beer mats, bottles, photos and furniture. In here the men tell many a yarn over a pint of Guinness.'

Guidelines for planning reminiscence in small groups

Deciding whether to do individual work or group work will depend upon the persons involved, the context in which you are working and the objectives you wish to achieve. Groupwork with people with dementia is certainly possible but groups need to be small – probably with no more than two to four members, who must be selected with great care. A small group makes it more possible for each member to be encouraged to participate, to have adequate time in which to do so and to feel their contribution is valued. Individual work may be preferable for many people as it provides rich opportunities for personal, concentrated attention and the development of a 'holding' relationship.

Some people with dementia, however, enjoy the company provided by membership of a small group which may counteract the encroaching isolation caused by their memory loss and associated language difficulties. In a small intimate group people seem to learn again the rules of conversation with others. The gains from mixing in a small group must be balanced with the problem many people with Alzheimer's disease have of keeping track of who said what in conversation.

People with dementia can also participate successfully in very small numbers in groups where the majority of members do not have obvious memory difficulties. Depending on particular circumstances they do not always need to be segregated in dementia-only groups. Even in a very small group it is helpful to have two leaders in order to give personal attention, to share tasks and to cope if anyone becomes upset or wishes to leave the group. With more helpers, groups can be a little larger.

Exclude from groupwork people who are very restless, hyperactive, or aggressive. People who are habitually tearful, preoccupied with a single obsessional recollection or who endlessly repeat the same word, phrase or noise can also be very disruptive. Consider working with them on a one-to-one basis instead.

Obtaining informed consent is important, but not always easy. Relatives may also need to give permission. Although most welcome the suggestion, there may be some who find the idea frightening or threatening and may not wish their family member to be involved. Always extend a simple, honest invitation, even if you think the person may not fully understand. Encourage people to come, remind them on the day and be finely tuned to non-verbal signs of pleasure or distress. Make it possible for people to indicate in whatever way they are able that they do not wish to participate. With restless people, it is best to leave the door of the meeting room ajar, and do not prevent anyone leaving if they so wish.

A person with dementia cannot be expected to call up specific memories on demand. You have to set the scene and provide the relevant and appropriate stimuli. Sessions may need to be shorter than an hour but many people with moderate dementia can retain interest much longer than is usually expected, provided the triggers and the topics are relevant. Adjust the length of the session according to the mood of the members, which will likely vary from meeting to meeting.

It is recommended that sessions be held more frequently than once a week. They should always be held in the same place, at the same time of day and follow the same pattern. Some workers like to provide familiarity and a sense of continuity by wearing the same clothes or perfume at each session. A regular structure or pattern to the group meeting, including identical opening and ending activities, like ritual songs or actions, provide continuity, security and stability.

Try to hold the group at the time of day when the members are more lucid. Careful observation will reveal what is their best time. As a rough general rule, many people with dementia seem to be more restless and disorientated in the late afternoon or twilight, perhaps because of altered visual cues caused by changing light and deepening shadows.

Multi-sensory triggers are especially important and they should closely relate to people's known background and previous interests. Do not overwhelm or overload people. Use triggers sparingly and selectively, usually one at a time.

> **Day centre worker** 'People with dementia come to our day centre for two days a week. It's in an area of the town where a lot of people live who once worked in the local mill so we have gathered up a lot of old bobbins, spools, wool and different types of cloth. We also have old newspapers with pictures of mills and mill workers, and our local museum gave us a recording of a mill hooter, a sort of siren which was blown at the start and end of the shift. We use all these things with two or three women together, or sometimes just with one person to get them talking.'

Speak with older friends, relatives and others with local knowledge so you can discover what triggers relate to the past life of the people with whom you plan to reminisce. You may be fortunate in being able to use people's own personal possessions. It is a real bonus if the group leaders share the same background as members and speak in a familiar accent or idiom.

Music is especially effective for people with dementia, but like all other interventions it must be used in a person-centred way. David Aldridge (1987) suggests music serves many functions, including calming people who are agitated; reducing wandering; improving self-esteem; stimulating memories and emotions; bringing people together; and lifting the spirit. Musical ability appears to be retained long after other abilities have deteriorated. Some people with no evidence of prior musical ability may be able to develop it, if given non-threatening opportunities.

Encourage people to sing along, to tap their feet, to sway, clap or dance. Words of once loved songs and hymns may be sung, sometimes spontaneously, sometimes with prompting, even when ordinary speech has deteriorated. Live music evokes rich response and gives great pleasure. It may also trigger sad recollections. Take the trouble to discover what kind of music each person may have enjoyed. Do not expect everyone to share the same tastes and ask relatives if they can provide previously loved tapes.

Music combined with physical movement or used together with other methods of sensory stimulation has proved effective. Simpler, slower and clearer melodies may come to be appreciated as much as old favourites. Nick Foster (1996), a researcher, has suggested that both novel and familiar background music played during a reminiscence session enhances autobiographical recall, although the reasons for this are not yet fully understood.

Nurse 'It was as a student nurse on my first ward that I first looked after an Alzheimer's patient. ... Mrs Smith was loud and it was impossible to have a conversation with her. She had a tendency to be violent, was agitated and she would not eat or drink.

'I started singing to her. At first she did not respond at all, but after a short time she began to join in. Not only did she know the words of all the songs but she had a wonderful singing voice. This woman who could not speak a coherent sentence could sing perfectly.'

Guidelines for specific prompted reminiscence work with individuals

If you are caring for particularly troubled and troubling individuals whose behaviour you find challenging, specific reminiscence is worth trying. Neurological damage caused by dementia, life experience and present circumstances will all be implicated in contributing to disruptive behaviour. Because these troubled people create so many difficulties for everyone around them – including other older people, family carers and professional carers – if you can make life better for them, you make life better for everyone else as well.

A note for senior staff

If specific work is to be undertaken which must involve giving more time and attention to an individual person, it is essential for senior staff to explain the care plan to all other staff, including care and domestic staff. Without such obvious backing from senior managers, any key worker chosen to undertake specific reminiscence work will feel lonely and unsupported. You may wish to refer back to the earlier discussion about the general need for senior managers' support (see pages 32–33).

If this support is not given, other staff will criticise them for neglecting ordinary duties and for paying too much attention to one person. The work attempted will be undermined and undone by other staff who have not been persuaded that it is right to single out someone, no matter how great their need, for concentrated personal attention. Work can be sabotaged in many different ways unless all the staff believe reminiscence and life story work are *real* work, as the following example shows:

Research worker 'Mary was selected for "specific" reminiscence work. She was a most unhappy, isolated, aggressive, underweight woman who pushed, hit, spat or shouted at anyone who came near. The key worker collected a detailed life history from Mary's niece and discovered that, when younger, Mary had always liked nice things such as fine china, good linen and small delicate flowers.

So the key worker decided to try to tempt her to eat by setting a breakfast tray with a linen tray cloth, special china and a posy of flowers. Mary started to eat better and some days she asked for a second piece of toast. Her aggression decreased and her isolation lessened. On the days when the key worker was off duty, the special arrangements were ignored because the cook refused to set the tray, so opposed was she to the idea of one resident being singled out for special attention. It took the officer in charge several weeks to confront the cook and instruct her not to undermine the care plan and to set the tray.'

Observation

Specific work must begin with careful observation over several days. Managers need to be willing to allow staff to pay concentrated particular attention to the selected person and to write detailed personal care plans, which will be reviewed from time to time. This may mean allocating more staff time. More often it means using staff time differently.

The work is based on careful, precise observation of present behaviour and detailed life history information used to illuminate the present.

Observations need to cover the daily pattern of the person so as to identify any recurring positive or negative features. Close observation draws a picture of the person's present lifestyle. It is advisable to observe:

- times of the day or night when the person may be especially happy or unhappy, disturbed, difficult, restless or agitated;
- time spent alone;
- interactions with other residents or staff;
- preferences for how and where the day is spent;
- the relevance, responsiveness and appropriateness of speech and behaviour;
- variations in mood, lucidity, activity and interests;
- behaviour around major events of the day such as getting up, bedtime, bathing, toileting and meals;
- ability to manage self-care and other activities of daily living;
- personal preferences for food, clothes, company and activities;
- reactions to visits by friends, family or volunteers.

Gathering life history details

Information about life history draws a picture of the person's past lifestyle which can then be used to help 'decode' present behaviour. The life history connects people to the present. So many older people with dementia who live in care resemble refugees. They are strangers in strange places, cut off from their past and alienated from the present. Life history, skilfully used, can link a distant past with a problematic present. It also enables carers to understand what may be troubling a person in the present.

If the history depends on what the person can tell about themselves, the past may remain very shadowy, just a fleeting glimpse. The details of the life history must therefore be collected from all possible sources, including the older person, their relatives, contemporaries and agency records.

Too frequently these records give only negative accounts of recent or present functioning. They tend to stress what people can no longer do and say little about what capacities remain and what interests might be revived. Imagine your own life to date summarised in just a few lines on an assessment form. This would not do justice to you now at a much younger age. Yet this is often all that is known about the long lives of so many older people in hospitals, nursing homes or residential homes.

Be sensitive but persistent in researching the life history. Try to pick up clues about significant past events, people and places. Keep careful records of what you learn.

Useful information includes the following:

- important chronological events such as births, deaths and marriages;
- childhood, school and student days;
- family life and work;
- significant friends and relationships;
- major life crises or trauma, landmarks, changes or branching points and transitions;
- where the war was spent and how it was experienced;
- places lived in or visited;
- hobbies, interests and recreation.

Start reminiscing with the older person. Learn to listen very attentively and respond to the expressed emotion. Conversation may need to be decoded or translated. Listen for recurring themes. Do not be preoccupied with establishing factual accuracy. Try to decipher the symbolic meanings and metaphors. If you begin by assuming truth rather than falsity, belief not disbelief, much valuable information can be gathered.

Stop labelling people as 'confused' and dismissing muddled conversation, especially if a person is obviously upset about struggling to tell you about something that has caused them hurt. Try to get sufficient clues to check it out with someone who may remember something from the past that has now 'leaked' into the present.

All too often when a person with dementia is upset, tearful or distressed about a past memory which has intruded into the present, workers hastily change the conversation, attempt distraction or denial. Some may even physically, or emotionally remove themselves from the conversation. Try to extend your ability to feel your way into the world of the other person. Be more willing to explore past pain and share past sadness. You may be able to piece together the fragments of the story (possibly illuminated by the life history you have gathered) which is causing distress at the present time. The following example illustrates the need for this kind of detective work.

Social worker 'Andy, who used to be a sociable friendly man, had an early-onset dementia. He had withdrawn into a world of silence, no longer even talking to his devoted wife who was determined to care for him at home. During a planned reminiscence session with him at a day centre when a collection of family photographs was being used to try to stimulate conversation, he was shown a picture of Niagara Falls. He launched at once into a long, apparently garbled tale about a woman who had thrown her baby over the Falls.

The worker thinking this was a bizarre fantasy hastily changed the conversation. Later, when checking back with his wife, every detail as told by Andy was found to be correct.'

Older relatives, especially spouses and partners, are often delighted to be asked for information. They feel they are contributing to the care of their person who, as the dementia progresses, is almost inevitably becoming a stranger. Positive benefits for the partner from this type of parallel reminiscence may also occur.

Another way of undertaking reminiscence has been developed by Yukiko Kurokawa (1996) who does couple reminiscence. She works with carefully selected couples, one of whom has dementia. They undertake a kind of mutual simultaneous life review together, using memories to share again and integrate their family experience. She suggests that by this process the well spouse is better able to cope with their partner's deterioration. This mutual journey is often given tangible form through the creation of a collage made from either photographs or pictures from magazines chosen by the participants to capture mood as well as memories.

Making a plan

When the detailed life history has been gathered, make a written plan of how the information is to be used. The plan is only a guide to a possible journey you and the person with whom you are working will take together. There will be unexpected detours, surprises, excitement, shared pleasure and, no doubt, some disappointments as well. You are beginning a demanding journey because at the same time you have to be finely tuned to present needs as well as to past history.

Implementing the plan

Use the history to introduce focused conversation, trips, visits to once-significant places, to re-introduce old hobbies or follow up old interests. The information you have collected will give clues to possible fruitful topics of conversation. You become an active memory bank on behalf of the other person, drawing on its rich deposits to benefit the actual owner in the present.

When the conversation is set in safe territory, people may be secure enough to risk responding. Ease them gently into situations and to conversations which emphasise what they can still do. They may be well aware of their deficiencies and need warm loving encouragement and time to respond.

Use life history to select triggers and arrange situations that resemble past experience. Helping with the cooking or the washing, trips to the seaside, a night at the greyhounds, a visit to the circus or an evening in the local pub can give immense pleasure to people with dementia who can often pass themselves in such situations without their dementia becoming apparent. Social circumstances and surroundings, if sufficiently familiar, can stir long-dormant memories and well-learned behaviour. The experience is enjoyed at the time, but it also provides a focus for future conversation and continuing pleasure.

Reviewing the work undertaken

Always take stock of what you have attempted. Give yourself credit for success and face up to failures. Such intensive work with individuals contributes to your own development. It helps you to learn that each person is unique and has distinct needs. It increases your confidence in being able to cope with troubled people. It brings great personal pleasure and job satisfaction when you see evidence of your own developing skills which improve life for an individual and for others who live and work with them.

You find that you can cope better with troubled and troubling people, decreasing their isolation and lessening their unhappiness. Because this kind of individual work changes relationships and lessens the distance between staff and older people, attitudes change, tolerance grows, sympathies are enlarged. You learn to be less frightened and less overwhelmed by the awfulness of dementia.

Officer in charge of specialist home 'Elizabeth always disrupted meal times by shouting and messing with her food. Her detailed life history showed she had always preferred to lie in and rise late. Instead, our staff were getting her up early, hurrying her to get dressed and to come downstairs for breakfast.

We decided to be more relaxed. She was left to sleep until she woke. Her key worker then helped her dress at her own pace. By the time she came downstairs, most people had finished breakfast and she could eat in solitude which seemed to suit her much better. Her shouting disappeared, she complained less about a sore back and she ceased to be a trouble to everyone else.'

Very occasionally, someone may have an over-reaction which is inappropriate to their present circumstances. This 'catastrophic reaction' is like an electric circuit becoming overloaded and an appliance blowing a fuse to save further damage. If this happens, try to stay calm; do not waste energy on trying to reason with the distressed person or talk them out of their exaggerated response. Gentle distraction and patience are the best response. Try to keep life simple with gentle routines that provide order without rigidity. Do not take the upset personally but think about whether something you did might have innocently provoked the outburst.

If something in a reminiscence session appeared to trigger the eruption, avoid those particular triggers, topics or associations. The behaviour may be totally unrelated to your reminiscence work, though, so do not hastily conclude that reminiscence has caused the distress.

The key to successful work is to appreciate the individual – as he or she used to be and now is.

Reminiscence, reality orientation and validation therapy

Reality orientation and validation therapy are both used with people with dementia. Reminiscence work is relevant to older people, regardless of whether or not they have dementia, although it requires adaptation for people with dementia.

Sometimes reminiscence and reality orientation are talked about as if they were identical because the two approaches in some ways resemble each other. They are, however, very different in their underlying ideas and values. Validation therapy has more in common with reminiscence as it, too, values a person's past and seeks to understand whatever appears presently to preoccupy the older person. It is important not to confuse these three different 'therapies'.

Reality orientation

Reality orientation (RO) was first introduced in psychiatric hospitals as a way of affirming older patients' uniqueness and humanity. Out of this emphasis on individuality, RO developed as a method for helping older people beset by failing memory to remain in touch with the present.

This was attempted in two ways. The first was by means of special classes or group activities that emphasised the here and now. The second was by 24-hour orientation implemented through consistent behaviour by all staff, and reminders or memory joggers within the care environment such as notice boards, calendars, large clocks, colour coding and labelling of doors. Such cues of course are help-ful to people with dementia whether or not RO is being practised.

Earlier enthusiasm for group RO has disappeared. Bob Woods (1994) now argues that while its original emphasis on individualis-ing care remains crucial, responding to people's emotions, sensitive cognitive retraining, using memory aids, focused memory training to help with particular needs, and attention to the designed envi-ronment are more effective.

Validation therapy

Feil (1992), who created validation therapy, describes it as:

'... the acceptance of an older person's struggle to restore the past, recognising it as a way to survive the bleak present. The technique allows us to communicate with, and to care for, confused older people more effectively.

'The validation worker respects the uniqueness of each disoriented per-son and realises that they are trying to survive loneliness and despair. The validation worker understands their struggle in this final stage of their life and chooses to walk beside them, wherever they happen to be.'

Validation therapy is used with very old people with advanced dementia. The therapist tries to listen to the words they use, then empathises with and interprets the feelings behind the words. It is undertaken with individuals and with groups. Both approaches, and the role of the validation therapist, are described by de Klerk-Rubin (1994; 1995).

Both reminiscence and validation therapy assume that an interest in the past life of older people is important for its own sake, not just as a means of keeping them in touch with present reality. Reminis-cence respects the past and uses it to help the older person retain a sense of identity and personhood.

KEY POINTS

- Communicating with people with dementia is possible but takes time.
- Reminiscence work requires adaptation for people with dementia.
- It is more effective in very small groups or with individuals.
- Reminiscence and other creative activities provide constructive roles for professional and family carers.
- Valuing a person's life story and using it with them in the present helps achieve person-centred care and retain a sense of person-hood.

Further Reading

Care-Giving in Dementia (Volume 2) by B Miesen and G Jones (eds). Routledge, London, 1997.

Narrative Identity and Dementia by M Mills. Ashgate, Aldershot, 1998.

Reminiscence in Dementia Care by P Schweitzer (ed). Age Exchange, London, 1998.

State of the Art in Dementia Care by M Marshall (ed). Centre for Policy on Ageing, London, 1997.

APPLICATION EXERCISES

1 Select a person with dementia whose behaviour worries or puzzles you. Try by every means available to collect detailed information about their life history. Then use your knowledge to increase the amount of time you spend together and the amount of genuine communication that takes place between you.

   Make notes about any changes you observe in your attitudes towards the person and your behaviour when you are with them.

   Discuss these changes with a fellow staff member.

2 Practise really listening (listening attentively) for five minutes to someone whom you consider is always talking in a very 'confused' way.

   Reflecting on this careful concentrated listening, what did you learn:

   a) about yourself?

   b) about the person?

3 Provide an opportunity for two or three people with dementia to reminisce together for several planned sessions. Identify the rewards and the difficulties. What was achieved and for whom?

9 Reminiscence with People who are Depressed

This chapter includes:

- Loss in later life
- Morale and types of reminiscers
- Choosing group or individual reminiscence work
- Using cherished objects in reminiscence

Loss in later life

Depression, a disorder of mood, is the biggest threat to mental health and wellbeing in old age. Various biological, psychological and social factors interact to predispose, precipitate and perpetuate each person's depression. In later life, depression may continue to affect people who have experienced earlier recurring depressive episodes. It may become apparent only in mid or later life as relationships and circumstances change or earlier unresolved problems re-emerge. As Warrington (1996) describes, it may be mistaken for a dementing illness, or occur simultaneously with dementia.

Depression in older people frequently goes unrecognised, unassessed and untreated. Because much depression can be treated effectively, such neglect, whether arising from ignorance or indifference, is unacceptable.

Loss is universal and inevitable as people grow older. It comes in many forms and challenges people's ability to cope and to enjoy life. It is not just loss of loved ones, a partner, husband or wife, friends and adult children. Physical health and strength, perhaps mental health as well, may diminish. The roles and responsibilities once carried with pride and satisfaction, disappear or diminish. Many people are obliged to move house, to scale down, to discard belongings. They experience the loss of familiar places, cherished possessions, gardens, pets and pastimes that were once significant.

It is impossible to understand the processes of ageing without understanding loss, grief and bereavement but there can also be gains, growth and satisfaction in later life. New relationships may blossom and new interests develop. Grandchildren may bring pleasure and a sense of continuity. Loss and relinquishment, however, remain a recurring, often dominating experience in later life. Accompanying feelings of numbness, shock, pain, longing, anger and guilt are common.

Bereaved people sometimes substitute illness for emotional reactions. Certainly, in the first 12 months after a major bereavement, demands on doctors are known to increase. When faced with loss, especially loss of someone very close, people are bewildered. The world as they knew it has suddenly changed. They find it hard to make sense of it, to locate themselves, to feel optimistic about the future and see the new directions which must be charted.

Gradually some measure of acceptance, hope and willingness to invest in new experiences begins to emerge, providing sufficient recovery time is available before they experience the next loss. Some people seem to cope better than others. In trying to understand why this is so, some writers suggest that people who experience a sense of coherence in their lives seem to be better protected against stress, which in turn protects from depression.

Faced with needing to develop new meanings and ways of coping, reminiscence is used by some older people to help solve problems. They use the recollection of past successful experience to help cope with present problems and reassure themselves about future coping. Reminiscence helps them to value past achievements and hence value themselves, even if the present is uncertain and the future full of threat. This is particularly true for those depressed people who manage to achieve a constructive reappraisal of the past and integrate a new understanding of their self-worth.

Various writers, identified by Watt and Cappeliez (1994) and Hunt, Marshall and Rowlings (1997), suggest that when advancing age brings the realisation that death is no longer far off but nearer at hand, some people may become very self-absorbed, sad or angry as old unresolved conflicts re-surface. Experiencing again these unresolved conflicts, this 'unfinished business', may trigger serious depression or despair.

Perhaps it is not so much old age as enforced retirement, at whatever age, or other major crises which trigger the process of life review. By the time people reach their seventies or eighties they have less unfinished business to attend to, and their spontaneous life review has already been largely completed.

Many older people appear to be demoralised, if not clinically depressed. Cumulative loss and bereavement, or unresolved or incomplete grieving from earlier losses, may lead to a state of chronic or permanent sadness. As people age, they scarcely have time to recover from one loss before they are confronted with the next. When losses come thick and fast with little time between for recovery, people may feel continually sad, overwhelmed, unable or unwilling to invest much energy in fresh beginnings.

Substantial numbers of people in the early stages of a dementing illness may be very well aware that they are losing their memory and that their independence and competence is being threatened. This can make them fearful, anxious, terrified and depressed. Both at this stage and later into their illness, some people, as Mills (1998) found, are well able to benefit from extended opportunities to discuss their life history or biography and to look again at past problems.

Living in residential homes, nursing homes and hospitals may be sufficient in itself to trigger deep regret, demoralisation or depression. The circumstances which led to the person being in care, rather than the care environment itself, may possibly hold the key to their depression.

Regretting their inability to live independently, perhaps older people in care are more likely to complain, to compare their present circumstances unfavourably with what went before, and to become preoccupied with repetitive obsessive reminiscence. They may use reminiscence as a way of preventing themselves from investing in the present. Used in this way, reminiscence may seem to be a kind of mourning or grieving process.

It is unlikely that life-long mental health problems will diminish with advancing age. Some depressed people who are inclined to be obsessional become preoccupied with looking back, but their guilt remains despite repeated telling of the same story. They may become stuck over one particular episode or period and be unable to move beyond it. They may use reminiscence, as Webster (1997) suggests, for 'bitterness revival', to 'keep memories of old hurts fresh'. Others may have struggled hard to reach some acceptance of their lives and they may have buried painful experiences that are now beyond conscious recall.

Some severely depressed people are so very unhappy and so absorbed in their present distress that they are not able to reminisce. They have neither the energy nor the interest to recall the past. Their self-acceptance and self-satisfaction may be so precarious that they do not wish to risk re-examining and re-interpreting their past. Working with such people requires skilled professional training.

Inexperienced reminiscence workers are often afraid they will stumble into painful aspects of a person's life and do more harm than good. It is as well to be aware of this possibility but do not let this anxiety prevent you beginning reminiscence work. The greater risk is in doing nothing, in leaving older, isolated, unhappy people unstimulated and unsupported. Provided that you are empathetic, responsive and have time for listening, you are unlikely to do harm. Do take notice though of what has been said about the need for supervision.

Very occasionally, an older person may experience such painful recall and such deep distress triggered by participating in a reminiscence activity that more skilled help will be required. If this happens, seek advice urgently from senior staff, who will know how to get further guidance from appropriate professionals in health and social service agencies.

People use reminiscence in different ways. Coleman (1986), a psychologist, identified four different types of people, ways in which they use reminiscence, and its influence on their morale. The table below, drawn from his findings, is a reminder that reminiscence does not suit everyone.

MORALE AND TYPES OF REMINISCERS		
1 Reminiscers	People who value memories of the past	High morale
2 Reminiscers	People troubled by memories of the past	Low morale
3 Non-reminiscers	People who see no point in reminiscing	High morale
4 Non-reminiscers	People who avoid reminiscing because of the contrast between their past and present	Low morale

So it is very important for you to try to understand each person's perspective on their life story. For the first group of people who reminisce readily, their memories are a source of strength which they and you can use as a resource in the face of difficulties. If faced with problems, a reminder that they have coped in the past may help encourage this sort of person to overcome present problems. Being reminded of their history, they can be helped to value it and to move on.

The second group brood on their memories, feeling regretful and sad. You will need to try to understand how rational or irrational such regrets are. Counselling may help these people to view their past and their understanding of it somewhat differently. Some people have very good reasons for feeling guilty about their past behaviour. They may feel even worse if the person they have wronged is now dead, so there is no opportunity to make amends. These troubled people may like to talk with a minister of religion or a counsellor, who may be able to help them to move from a sense of guilt to a sense of forgiveness and acceptance.

The third group should be helped to get on with the things they consider are important to them. They should not be forced to contemplate their past. If they are 'doers', your task is to help them get on with doing whatever is important to them, here and now.

The fourth group say their past lives were happy, but reminiscence makes them sad when they do not need to be, so they avoid thinking and talking about the past. Unless these people can come to terms with the changes and loss in their lives, they are likely to remain depressed.

Choosing group or individual reminiscence work

Reminiscence with people who are depressed must therefore be undertaken with great care. Present depression can influence the content of reminiscence in that memories of past sadness may dominate the recall process. It may be easier for depressed people to respond to individual work where they may feel freer to reveal intimate details or talk about parts of their past life that have caused them pain. In these circumstances, individual work is more likely to foster a close, confiding relationship between the older person and the reminiscence worker.

In a group, however, the depressed person, provided that they have sufficient energy to participate and do not feel ignored, may well find their peers to be supportive, constructively reassuring. If they can be helped to feel safe, they may be eased into making new relationships. This may be particularly so if people discover common ground, the shared experience of painful loss and transitions. Older people know more about coping with hurt, grief and loss than younger people. Pain shared in a warm accepting group may be healed or at least reduced.

In responding to depression, efforts to impart a feeling of independence and control will be very important. Reminiscence can be used as a means of restoring some control to the person, who may at the very least be helped to control the process of recalling, and perhaps recording in some way, their own past life.

If the reminiscence process seems unhelpful, alternative assistance may need to be considered. Telling the story may not always be healing – for some people it may lead to further self-preoccupation. Counselling of various types or methods relying on non-verbal communication may be more effective.

As people approach death, some may be fearful, others hopeful. Some may use reminiscence as death preparation. Those without a sense of continuity, for whatever reason, may experience a sense of profound regret, of missed opportunity, of chances forgone, and of being cheated or short-changed.

For people who have always invested much of themselves in their work, some written or pictorial account of their life may provide reassurance. Tangible evidence that life has been worthwhile, or, if not worthwhile, at least not in vain, may bring reassurance. Placing themselves visually in the context of their wider family through researching and drawing a family tree helps some people achieve a sense of self-acceptance, coherence, continuity and resolution.

Autobiographical writing, including guided group autobiographical writing, helps to develop new perspectives. Seeking forgiveness, reconciliation and making reparation may be a part of this process. Also visits, pilgrimages, family reunions and writing to people who have links or connections with the past have all proved helpful when used as supported activities encouraged within caring relationships.

Looking back and looking forward embraces emotional, social and practical dimensions. Working on a life story book, organising the family photographs, doing a collage, making a story board, giving cherished possessions to people who are personally significant, making a will, assigning enduring power of attorney, and writing an advanced directive are tangible ways in which people can be helped to evaluate and order their lives.

Using cherished objects in reminiscence

'Memorabilia' refers to things or objects that stir recollection. Research suggests that people who have no available cherished objects experience a much lower mood and reduced life satisfaction compared with others in similar circumstances who have access to cherished objects.

Cherished possessions are thought to provide a sense of historical continuity, comfort and a sense of attachment or belonging. For people who have moved from the familiar to the unfamiliar, such objects may be very important because they give a feeling of ownership and control, and perceived control is known to be influential in creating a sense of wellbeing.

Cherished objects also provide opportunities to encourage reminiscence. They often seem to have a greater significance for women than for men. These treasured objects could provide a focus for individual or group reminiscence. For example, residents in a nursing or residential home could be invited to bring a special object to a session and to talk about its significance. Any attempt to use personal possessions for group reminiscence must be sensitive to the members who have none and may be mourning their loss. It is preferable if all members are able to bring something, but if this is not possible they could be asked to describe, or perhaps draw an object which had significance for them. Reminiscence work undertaken in a person's own home has limitless opportunities ready to hand.

It is sad that so many people admitted to care neither bring with them nor retain access to cherished objects. Staff concerned with assessment, admission and care management must take responsibility for ensuring that people entering care bring cherished possessions with them. Older people, family members and professional carers may need to be helped to understand the therapeutic importance of cherished objects and other kinds of memorabilia.

KEY POINTS

■ It is important to understand about depression, grief and loss in later life.

■ People need to be encouraged to express their pain as well as to value their achievements.

■ Be aware that reminiscence is used by different people for different purposes. Older people and their families should be encouraged to retain and to use cherished objects to enrich the present.

APPLICATION EXERCISES

1 Write down a list of key words that come to mind when you think of depression in general. Now think of a particular old person you know whom you would describe as 'depressed'.

What words would you apply to them?

Compare and contrast the two lists.

2 Considering the particular person you have thought of, can you suggest some reminiscence-type activities that might interest them?

Discuss your ideas with a senior colleague, adviser or supervisor.

If they agree, undertake some planned individual work with the identified person.

Further Reading

'Reminiscence interventions for the treatment of depression in older adults' by L M Watt and P Cappeliez. In *The Art and Science of Reminiscing: Theory, research, methods and applications* by B K Haight and J D Webster (eds). Taylor and Francis, London, 1995.

Depression and Dementia: Co-existence and differentiation by J Warrington. Dementia Services Development Centre, Stirling, 1996.

Past Trauma in Late Life by L Hunt, M Marshall and C Rowlings (eds). Jessica Kingsley, London, 1997.

10 Reminiscence with People with Hearing, Sight and Speech Disabilities

This chapter includes:

- Creating opportunities for participation
- Hearing problems
- Visual problems
- Speech problems

As people grow older, hearing and sight problems become increasingly common. People with strokes are often left with speech problems. None of these difficulties should automatically prevent them from taking part in reminiscence. Provided that proper care is taken, involvement in reminiscence can lessen social isolation, restore a sense of self-worth and assist in improving a person's quality of life. Unfortunately, increasing age combined with one or more communication problems can leave people very lonely and isolated, even if they are living surrounded by others.

Creating opportunites for participation

Careful assessment of each individual is needed. Consider their own wishes and preferences, and work out together, possibly in conjunction with relatives, how best to help them to participate in reminiscence.

The more limited a person's ability to communicate, the more appropriate individual work, rather than groupwork, is likely to be. This is only a general working principle because many people with sensory problems can and do manage to participate successfully in small groups. The presence of multiple sensory disabilities, with the possible addition of dementia will multiply the complexity of all reminiscence work.

It will be necessary to adjust the size of a group, how it is run and what trigger materials are used to make it possible for members with sensory problems to benefit. There are really three parties to any decision about whether a person with a serious sensory handicap should join a group. First, the person with the disability needs to be consulted. Explain to them carefully what is proposed. Make sure they have understood what has been said. Second, the leader needs to decide whether or not he or she is sufficiently competent to cope. Third, the other potential group members may need to be consulted, because special demands will be made on them. Advice from specialist staff may also be helpful.

If a potential member is uncertain about whether or not to join a group, encourage them to come once or twice to try it out, to see how well they can manage, before making up their minds.

So often, professional carers make decisions on behalf of older people, especially those with disabilities, instead of letting them decide for themselves. Be sensitive to attitudes and actions by staff that restrict opportunities and exclude people from activities which they could enjoy.

The following example from a residential home shows how the Officer in Charge thought she knew what was best for people when she advised the reminiscence worker:

'Don't bother including Mr B. Since his stroke he is very hard to understand and he will not be able to join in.'

The worker persisted and included Mr B in a small group. Later he reported:

'Mr B was very slow to join in at first. Then I showed him the horseshoe and he became very excited and was determined to speak. He responded to everything and people were very patient listening to him.'

If a group has a mixed membership which includes some people with a disability, its size and make-up need very careful thought.

Small groups with a co-leader are likely to work best. The co-leader can sit near the person with the disability and assist in various ways. Group members too are very resourceful, for as Michael Bender (1994), a clinical psychologist, argues, 'the wisdom is in the group.'

Small groups consisting of members with similar disabilities are more manageable than a mixed group with people with various disabilities where it is hard to attend to everyone's different needs. If the group consists of some members with a disability and others with none, probably no more than two people with disabilities should be included.

The dual demand to attend simultaneously to the group and to all the individuals within it is quite hard to manage at times. Inexperienced leaders may find themselves initially either ignoring the needs of a single member or alternatively paying them so much attention that the needs of the group are sacrificed. So much goes on, even in a very small group, that it is difficult to be aware of everything, let alone respond appropriately. Honest feedback between co-leaders as well as discussion with a supervisor or consultant is very important in developing self-awareness and a capacity for self-reflection.

A varied collection of multi-sensory triggers can help stimulate discussion and assist everyone, despite their disability, to participate. If people are unable to respond to one kind of trigger, another type may prove effective. Take care to ensure helpful seating arrangements and good light. Use clear, well-modulated speech. Other suggestions are listed on pages 109–110.

Lack of confidence and low self-esteem often prevent people from joining groups. They fear making fools of themselves or being a burden to others. This means that you may have to work especially hard to help people with hearing, speech and visual problems to feel comfortable enough to be prepared to join. Reminiscence can be an effective way of breaking down barriers because it is usually so enjoyable and gives immediate and infectious pleasure. The shared good fun and intimate discussion encourage further growth in confidence which in turn brings increasing participation.

Hearing problems

Hearing problems make participation in groups extremely difficult. If a person wears a hearing aid which magnifies all noise, large groups become exceedingly uncomfortable. However, in a small group, with good lighting and appropriate seating to assist lip-reading, and triggers that do not rely greatly on sound, many deaf people will be able to enjoy a reminiscence group.

The visual stimulation provided by 35-mm slides will have to be weighed against the disadvantage of reduced lighting which makes lip-reading impossible. Enlarged pictures and various other triggers which rely on sight, touch, taste and smell can be very effective with people with hearing problems.

The level of frustration that people with acquired and progressive hearing loss experience is tremendously varied. Some will enjoy being part of a small group, even if hearing is difficult. Others will be so distressed over what they fear they are missing that their predicament is worsened.

Do not shout when communicating with people with a hearing impairment. Clear, careful speech with rephrasing is crucial. When you shout, the increased volume means that the tone is usually raised. Because many older people lose their capacity to hear high tones and consonants, shouting does not help. Rather than repetition, rephrasing which uses different sound patterns will increase the likelihood of hearing and hence understanding.

Lip-reading classes for older people can make good use of reminiscence. Being interested in the subject matter, they will listen more attentively and speak more freely. In this way, reminiscence assists and lip-reading skills 'are caught, rather than taught', as is often suggested.

Provided that appropriate communication skills are used, people who were born deaf are as likely as anyone else to enjoy and profit from reminiscence. Ideally, trained interpreters who are also skilled in running reminiscence groups should be used, but this is not always possible. A compromise is for a reminiscence groupworker to be assisted by an interpreter or sign language helper. Workers must get to know each other and to understand and respect each other's contribution. Different skills will be needed as people may use lip-reading and lip-speaking, finger-spelling, British Sign Language, Irish Sign Language or total communication. Also remember that people from ethnic minority groups may not have mastered English and language problems will be worsened by any speech or hearing impairment.

Many amplification aids are available. They include conventional hearing aids, induction loops, battery-operated communicators and conversers, amplifiers and radio microphones. Seek advice and information from specialist workers such as speech and language therapists, hearing therapists, audiologists, special teachers, social workers for the deaf or doctors before buying any special equipment.

Information is usually available from social services departments and specialist agencies such as the Royal National Institute for Deaf People and the Disabled Living Foundation.

Visual problems

Reminiscence can be effective both with people who are born blind and with those who become visually impaired in later life. Visual images acquired from past experience, hearing, reading, touch and smell can be used to evoke reminiscence. A person's store of visual images can be enriched and expanded by verbal descriptions which may then become triggers to stimulate recall of associated memories.

The memories of people who have become blind are often crystal clear, uncluttered by more recently acquired visual images. As a consequence, these people can be valuable historical informants in a group with sighted members. Triggers with a multi-sensory appeal are invaluable. Objects that can be handled, tastes and smells, sounds, including reading aloud and music, are all effective.

Some people may need to have their vision checked. Many low vision aids, ranging from a simple magnifying glass to very sophisticated technological aids, are available. As with hearing impairment, seek specialist advice. Information and assistance are available from opticians, doctors, librarians, social services staff, the Royal National Institute for the Blind and other specialist agencies.

Speech problems

Reminiscence is one way of encouraging older people who have impaired speech following a stroke or who have Parkinson's disease or other conditions to practise talking. It can also be a useful way of involving relatives who may find encouraging speech practice a chore. As with lip-reading, if people are interested in what they are talking about, the amount of conversational practice they are prepared to undertake can be significantly increased.

Try to obtain an assessment by a speech and language therapist through your local health centre or social services department so that you understand the nature of the person's difficulties. Problems with understanding or with expressing understanding in speech, or a mixture of both, will respond to different approaches. It is best to seek specialist advice.

Self-consciousness is often forgotten in the excitement of reminiscing. The person with the speech problem is able to share their recall with others who in turn become less weary, frustrated or embarrassed by the limited communication.

Work in pairs may be more appropriate, but do not automatically rule out small group reminiscence. People should be given the chance to make their own choice, rather than have to endure the limitations imposed by someone who thinks they know best.

For example, a woman of 92 in residential care would often say: 'I don't speak so well since I had that stroke.' But as a member of a reminiscence group she spontaneously recited a long poem about the part of the country where she had farmed for many years. Other members were very moved and were quick to applaud: 'Marvellous. Marvellous. She has a good memory anyhow.'

Some people who cannot speak coherently, perhaps because of a stroke or dementia, may still be able to sing because this area of their brain has not been damaged. It is well worth experimenting in case it may be possible to encourage a singing response to 'conversational' singing which you initiate.

Conclusion

The greater the communication problems, the greater the care you will need to take in assessment and in selecting and using suitable multi-sensory triggers. A detailed life history will help you to identify personal interests and possible triggers which can then be exploited to the full.

Written and visual triggers, music, mime, gesture and drawing will all have a part to play. After considering the best professional advice, let your imagination run free. Follow your own intuition and sensitive inclinations in developing novel approaches to people who may otherwise remain extremely isolated and very frustrated.

KEY POINTS

- Observe carefully. Consult widely.
- Do not make premature judgements that exclude people with sensory and speech difficulties from reminiscence opportunities.
- Obtain specialist advice, including information about technical equipment, aids and adaptations.
- Be prepared to co-work with communication specialists.
- Develop non-verbal as well as verbal communication skills.

APPLICATION EXERCISES

1 Identify a person with a hearing, visual or speech problem. Consider how best to involve them in reminiscence work. Implement your ideas and then discuss the outcomes with a colleague.

2 Read about hearing, visual and speech problems in later life. How can this new learning benefit the people with whom you work?

Further Reading

Deafness by J Ballantyne, M Martin and A Martin (eds). Whurr, London, 1993.

Communication Problems in Elderly People: Practical approaches to management by R Gravell. Croom Helm, London, 1988.

'The needs and problems of older people with a visual impairment: historical, current and future perspectives' by M Davis. In: *British Journal of Visual Impairment* 14; 2: pp 53–57.

Social Skills and the Speech Impaired by L Rustin and A Khur. Singular Publishing, London, 1996.

11 Reminiscence with People with Learning Disabilities

This chapter includes:

- Benefits of reminiscence for people with learning disabilities
- The expression of loss and grief
- Locating, preserving and using relevant triggers
- The importance of making a tangible record

Reminiscence with people with learning disabilities can fulfill the same general functions described in Chapter 2. Each time planned reminiscence work with either individuals or groups is undertaken, the purpose and objectives need to be clear so these can guide the workers and enable them to explain what is intended to the participants. Published accounts of reminiscence work with people with moderate and severe learning disabilities demonstrate clearly that reminiscence work in groups and life history writing with individuals is greatly valued, indeed cherished by many of those involved. Reminiscence enables people with learning disabilities to look back on their lives, recall past experience, and reflect on its significance for themselves and for others.

Some modifications or adaptations are necessary, just as they have been necessary when working with other groups whose members have various disabilities. The guidance contained in earlier chapters on dementia, depression and sensory impairment is also relevant here. Once again there are reports from staff who say how surprised they are to find how well many people with a learning disability are able to participate; how previously undemonstrated and unrecognised abilities emerge and personal confidence develops in reminiscence groups.

Michael Bender (1994) identified these and other valuable outcomes for people with moderate and severe learning difficulties who participated in reminiscence groups lasting for at least ten sessions. He noted:

- improvement in verbal ability;
- clear expression of strong emotions, particularly concerning experiences of loss;
- self-control and patience, contrary to usual behaviour;
- absence of socially unacceptable behaviour;
- abandonment, within the group, of usual roles and habitual ways of presentation;
- demonstration of a sense of agency, or control over their own selves and circumstances.

The expression of loss and grief

When small reminiscence groups are held, many individual and collective recollections of painful memories, loss and grief are usually recounted. People with learning disabilities, especially as children and young people, even if living at home, were often protected from death in the family and not given opportunities by families and professional carers to openly mourn and to grieve when faced with bereavement and loss. Many have also lacked opportunities to talk openly about their own experience of rejection and awareness of being 'different' and how this has affected their lives.

In the past, many people with a learning disability were admitted to large institutions, often in infancy or childhood, thereby losing contact with their families and the neighbourhoods where they once lived. Having spent most of their lives in long-stay hospitals, people had to face enormous changes as the hospitals closed. They have been relocated in the community, in residential or nursing homes, hostels, small group homes or independent flats. For many the change in lifestyle has been dramatic.

Opportunities to mourn both the distant past and the more recent hospital past, no matter what it was like, are very necessary. The hospitals in which people spent so much of their lives should be actively acknowledged as a significant part of their life experience and hence of their memories. Except for the mental handicap hospital, many people with learning disabilities have no other sense of a significant place and its associated people.

Location, preservation and use of relevant triggers

So the trigger materials used to encourage reminiscence should relate to the known past, wherever it has been lived. As hospitals contract, close or are demolished and people transferred or resettled, it is crucial that records and personal remembered accounts of this historical heritage are not lost.

Collections of photographs portraying many aspects of hospital life usually exist somewhere, because these hospitals were themselves communities. It may be possible to locate photographs of holidays, sports days, trips, fetes, farms, workshops, special occasions, staff and patients. Try to recover and preserve this heritage for the sake of the people whose lives it represents. For many who grew up in hospital, staff and other patients have been a substitute family; for some, their only family. They will have many stories to tell, both good and bad, happy and sad, about staff, patients, friends, ill-treatment, punishments, jobs, kindness, recreation and the whole complex life of the hospital as a living community.

The same rules of good practice with individuals and groups apply to reminiscence work with people with learning disabilities and do not need to be repeated. Groups will require co-workers, and individual life story work can often be assisted and continuity assured if shared with more than one 'hearer'. When deciding on group membership, selection of people with a similar range of verbal abilities, including speed of speech, is recommended. It is not possible to be prescriptive about the number of sessions but at least ten and often many more is suggested. If it is planned to work on a group book or to assist an individual person to write their life story, several years may be necessary, as Dorothy Atkinson (1994), an oral historian and reminiscence worker, found.

Use carefully selected multi-sensory triggers. Tangible objects have proved very evocative. Do not overload people nor bombard them with questions. Adjust the pace of working and perhaps shorten the interval between sessions. Members' recollections will spark off other memories within the group so that at times a collective view, rather than a collection of individual memories, is achieved. Do not persist when attention span is limited. Be finely tuned to feelings. Help people express their pain, their frustrations and joy in their own way, at their own pace.

If people with learning disabilities are taking part in a group with other members and leaders whose life experience has been very different, be alert to any lack of shared common interests that may leave some people feeling inadequate or isolated. Alternately, they may be surprised to discover that they too have a story to tell and others are interested in hearing it.

Reminiscence looks back, but effective work also concerns the present and invests in the future. As people accumulate new life experiences, make a record, be building for the future. Take photographs, collect memorabilia, help compile a diary and preserve the life history for future use. Make the records concrete, attractive, simple and direct.

Remember too that recreational group reminiscence activities may be fruitful. Trips, pilgrimages, dances, organised games and outings may all be used to reinforce a sense of personal identity, to give pleasure, increase sociability and assist communication.

The importance of making a tangible record

Life story work is particularly relevant because of its emphasis on making tangible, practical, written or pictorial records of personal history. Never take for granted, or fail to appreciate, the fact that you can write your own story. If you choose to, you are capable of making your own record. People with learning disabilities may be able to tell you about themselves but may be unable to either write or read their stories. Do not assume this means that the tangible, durable record is not valued. Its importance must not be underestimated.

The process of recall is important but so too is the sense of permanence and significance which the product or record conveys. It is immensely prized, as Doreen Cocklin (1990) testified when her spoken-but-written, revealing observation was published in an anthology of prose, poetry and art by people with learning disabilities: 'This is the first time anything I have said has been written down'.

There will be a heavy reliance on the spoken, rather than the written word. Some people may be able to write but many will need a scribe, as Atkinson (1998) explains, to present their work in a way which makes it possible for others to appreciate it.

To assist the writing, reminiscence and life history workers frequently use a tape recorder and then a 'scribe' becomes responsible for producing the record. These transcriptions need to be read back, meticulously corrected or changed to make sure the story is being told as its owner intended. A copy of the tape and the writing should always be given to people to keep but can then be used effectively as a prompt for further reminiscence and recall. Community publishing and desktop publishing have meant that increasing numbers of 'silent' or 'invisible' people, not only those with learning disabilities, can now get their stories published, read and more widely appreciated. These accounts are significant contributions to developing understanding of others' experience, and the ways in which marginalised and excluded people have been denied past opportunities, so easily taken for granted by most of us.

The life story is important for the teller but it is also important for the hearer – herein lies the mutual gain for all involved, as Mabel Cooper (1998) shows. She was born in 1944, admitted to a children's home as a baby, at age 12 transferred to St Lawrence's Mental Handicap Hospital, then, after some 20 years, re-located in the community via time spent in a half-way hostel. She became actively involved in the self-advocacy movement, and now travels internationally and undertakes consultancy and staff training. Her story, told in her own words, with the assistance of a scribe, is published in the book by Atkinson, Jackson and Walmsley listed in 'Further Reading' on page 151.

She is quoted by Atkinson (1998) when she reflects on the experience of 'writing' the autobiography:

> 'It was very important to me to tell them about St Lawrence's and the way it was when I was there. And it's been a great joy, I've enjoyed it. Some of it hurts, some of it's sad, some of it I would like to remember. I keep the tapes with it on and I sit and listen to them. So it's something I want anyway, and I will keep it. I think it's good really, to think about what happened to you when you were a child. I think it's great. It's something.'

Atkinson then comments on how this work impacts on the workers, the scribes or ghost writers, including herself:

> '… who have been touched, moved and angered by their revelations. These stories have helped open our eyes to what life has been like for those people who, in the earlier years of the century, had the misfortune to enter the separate and closed world of the long-stay institutions.'

For as we get to know those who share their reminiscences and their life stories with us, we too gain, not just knowledge or vicarious experience, but an enlargement of our capacity to feel with others whose lives have been, and may still be, very different from our own.

This work is complex and demanding. It is important to consider very closely what people who are reminiscing actually say while they are reminiscing. You have to ask yourself what meaning the story has for the teller in the here and now. It will be a story about the past but it will be told in a particular way in the present context. This applies to all reminiscence but is particularly relevant to reminiscence with people with learning disabilities and people with dementia who are likely to have difficulty in explaining the meanings themselves.

The story that people tell is always influenced by the listener. The teller and the hearer are both creators of the story and no talk is meaningless. People with learning disabilities also have a story to tell. They, as much as anyone else, need someone to ask and someone to listen.

KEY POINTS

- The past is important for people with learning disabilities.
- Work in imaginative ways to help people to achieve a tangible record.
- This record, in turn, becomes a tool for continuing communication.
- Reflect on the impact which other people's stories make on you.

APPLICATION EXERCISES

1 Identify a person with a learning disability with whom you could work to compile a record of his or her life story. Collect photographs and memorabilia as well as actively preserving information now that will become part of the 'record' for the future.

2 Think about the ways you may need to adapt general and specific reminiscence work for individuals and small groups of people who have learning disabilities.

Further Reading

Forgotten Lives: Exploring the history of learning disability by D Atkinson, M Jackson and J Walmsley (eds). Bild Publications, Kidderminister, 1997.

Looking Back, Looking Forward: Reminiscence with people with learning disabilities by M Stuart. Pavilion, London, 1997.

Using Autobiographical Approaches with People with Learning Difficulties by D Atkinson and J Walmsley (forthcoming).

12 How to Develop Reminiscence Work and Sustain Good Practice

This chapter includes:

- Developing an action plan
- Reminiscence training and networking

Developing an action plan

It is almost impossible to develop good practice if you are working in isolation. Get colleagues and friends around you who will support, encourage and sustain each other's work.

Develop your own local resource materials. Start where you are with the people with whom you want to reminisce. Collect triggers that will mean something to them.

Use commercially marketed triggers only if you are unable to obtain your own or if you want to extend your own collection without too much trouble. Commercial packages will get you started and give you ideas but they are usually expensive. The same amount of money spent on acquiring local resources may give better returns.

Local schools and further education colleges may have photographic dark rooms, colour photocopiers, computers with scanners, laser printers and other useful equipment. They may be very pleased to cooperate in a reminiscence project. In return you may be able to help identify older people who would be willing to become historical informants and informal teachers. You may also be able to open up opportunities for younger students to undertake community service. Various aspects of the curriculum, not just history or community studies, can be enriched through the involvement of older people.

Partnerships between different agencies which bring together the statutory and independent service sectors can release creative energy to help develop and sustain reminiscence work. Librarians and museum staff are invaluable allies.

There are a lot of resources available to help you develop good reminiscence practice but there are no short cuts. Appendix 3 identifies some relevant organisations.

Do not hog your triggers or monopolise resources. Try to form a local group or network which meets from time to time to share ideas, constructively criticise work in progress and pool assets. You will all be the richer for sharing, and the quality of the reminiscence work you do will benefit.

This handbook has stressed co-operation. It emphasises the importance of both informal collaboration and formal supervision which itself may take different forms such as tandem or paired, team and group supervision. Find people whom you can trust to be honest with you, not tell you what you want to hear. Only by looking critically at your practice will you become more skilled. Training before you begin is important but further training needs to be linked to practice so that critical reflection becomes an integral part of your on-going development.

As the practice of care in the community develops, more older frailer people are being helped to remain in their own homes. As a consequence, we can expect more reminiscence work to be undertaken with individuals living in the community. As well as continuing to develop reminiscence work in hospitals, homes and day centres, it is increasingly important to help families, friends, volunteers and domiciliary care workers to understand how significant the past is and how they can encourage people to talk about it. An 11-country EU-funded European Reminiscence Network project, *Remembering Yesterday, Caring Today* is developing trans-national training materials to assist family carers of people with dementia to under-take reminiscence work at home. Various other projects and agencies, including volunteer bureaux, are training and using volunteers to work in institutions and in people's own homes.

Care management arrangements, strict financial controls, the precise definition of functional tasks and associated rationing of time spent by health and social care staff bring increasing pressures, which too often work against the development of good reminiscence practice. The tendency to regard care as a commodity and its recipients as consumers creates problems. This handbook does not apologise for arguing that older people's minds and souls (or spirits) need nourishment as much as their bodies. Relationships nurtured by effective communication are essential. Reminiscence and other creative activities are not expendable luxuries; they are life sustaining essentials.

Research using both qualitative and quantitative methodologies about reminiscence in different cultures, contexts of practice and with different types of reminiscers must be pursued so that our knowledge, understanding, and skill continue to develop. So far, most research has concentrated on outcomes with older people. Research needs to examine the relevance of and the functions served by reminiscence for men and women at earlier stages of the life cycle. The effect of reminiscence on staff, carers and volunteers awaits systematic enquiry.

Some of the groups and practice contexts awaiting experimental enquiry, practice exploration and theorising include reminiscence with younger people at various points in the life cycle; reminiscence work with prisoners, refugees, people with trauma-induced brain damage, Aids-related dementia, and dementia linked to learning disability. The process of reminiscence as much as its outcomes needs careful scrutiny. We need to learn more about the complex interdependence of the cognitive and creative aspects of reminiscence and recall, and how to harness this energy to improve communication and enhance wellbeing. The who, what, when, where, how and why of reminiscence all need careful attention.

Reminiscence training and networking

A large number of unaccredited training days, conferences and short courses, most of which award attendance certificates, are offered by various statutory and voluntary organisations, independent trainers and consultants. This training can often be arranged in response to local requests and may be offered on an in-house basis. Various organisations offering local or regional training are listed in Appendix 3. This list does not claim to be comprehensive. Local and regional training creates opportunities to establish links with other interested, accessible people who can support each other in developing good practice.

The University of Greenwich accredits some Age Exchange courses which by means of credit accumulation and transfer can lead to recognised awards of the University.

Further information on these courses is available from Age Exchange (address on page 177).

The European Reminiscence Network, based at Age Exchange, maintains a database of workers and provides opportunities through workshops, cross-national projects, publications, training programmes, theatre tours and international conferences for people to share experience and develop creative innovative practice. A subscription to *Reminiscence Magazine* is the best way of keeping abreast of Network developments.

See Appendix 2 for information about National Vocational Qualifications (NVQs) and Scottish Vocational Qualifications (SVQs).

The Open University's Level 1 certificate course, *Understanding Health and Social Care*, carries 60 Cats points and relates to N/SVQ Levels 3 and 4 in Care. It is designed to provide knowledge, skills and understanding required in caring work of all kinds. One study block, *Working with Life Experience* is of special relevance to reminiscence work.

Further information is available from the Information Officer, School of Health and Social Welfare, Open University, Walton Hall, Milton Keynes MK7 6AA; tel: 01908 653743.

The University of Sussex offers various courses in oral history and reminiscence, including two part-time, year-long courses, the Certificate in Life History Work and a Postgraduate Diploma in Adult Learning and Life Histories. A one-year full-time or two-year part-time MA in Life History Research is also available.

For further information, contact the Centre for Continuing Education, University of Sussex, Brighton BN1 9RG; tel: 01273 606755, ext 3585; fax: 01273 678848; e-mail: a.s.thomson@sussex.ac.uk.

Conclusion

Do continue to read about reminiscence work. Some suggestions are listed in the 'Further Reading' lists at the end of each chapter. As you read, try to distinguish between reports of actual reminiscence work, empirical research studies, particular methods or approaches and theory-building articles. You will be able to learn from research articles and analyses of good practice but when you go to apply the ideas you will need to copy, as best you can, the same conditions described in the article in order to try out the same approach. Reading about others' experience of reminiscence work will give you new ideas about fresh directions as well as increase your own confidence in what you are doing.

Remember that one meaning of 'professional' is trying to do better tomorrow what you have done today. No matter how well your work has gone so far, you will still be able, next time, to become a more attentive listener, a more empathic person, a more sensitive, skilled worker. Consolidate your development by undertaking some more reminiscence work very soon. In this way you will build on what you have already learned rather than letting it become submerged by other pressing demands on your time and attention.

To help you look to your future reminiscence work, with all its rich possibilities for benefiting both yourself and older people, you may like to complete one last exercise.

KEY POINTS

- Co-operative working, networking and supervision encourage good practice.
- Training, critical reflection and continued reading are important.
- Reminiscence and recall with individuals and small groups requires further research.

APPLICATION EXERCISES

1 Divide a sheet of paper into four columns.

In column 1 list the obstacles in your workplace or circumstances which prevent you from doing the kind of reminiscence work, with either individuals or groups, which you think it is important to do and would like to do.

In column 2 list the obstacles in yourself that get in the way of this work.

In column 3 identify the action you intend to take to overcome the obstacles listed in columns 1 and 2.

In column 4 place a date by which you intend to have taken the actions identified in column 3.

2 If possible, discuss with a colleague what you have written.

3 In six months time, check back. Give yourself credit and criticism for what has happened in the meantime.

Further Reading

Consult the *Reminiscence Database*, *Reminiscence Magazine* and *Journal of Dementia Care* (see Appendix 3).

REFERENCES

Aldridge D (1987) *Music Therapy Research and Practice in Medicine: From out of the silence.* London: Jessica Kingsley.

Atkinson D (1994) '"I got put away": Group-based reminiscence with people with learning difficulties.' In: Bornat J (ed). *Reminiscence Reviewed: Perspectives, evaluations and achievements.* Buckingham: Open University Press, pp96–104.

Atkinson D (1998) 'Autobiography and learning disability.' In: *Oral History* 26; 1: pp73–80.

Barr-On D (1995) *Fear and Hope: Three generations.* Newhaven: Harvard University Press.

Bartlett E (ed) (1992) *Nice Tastin': Life and food in the Caribbean.* London: Chelsea Community History Group.

Bender M (1994) 'An interesting confusion: What can we do with reminiscence groupwork?' In: Bornat J (ed). *Reminiscence Reviewed: Perspectives, evaluations and achievements.* Buckingham: Open University Press, pp32–45.

Birren J E and Birren B A (1996) 'Autobiography: exploring the self and encouraging development'. In: Birren J, Kenyon G, Ruth J E, Schroots J and Svensson T (eds). *Aging and Biography.* New York: Springer, pp283–299.

Bornat J (1989) 'Oral history as a social movement: reminiscence and older people.' In: Perks R and Thompson A (eds). *The Oral Reader.* London: Routledge, pp189–205.

Butler R (1963) 'The life review: an interpretation of reminiscence in the aged.' In: *Psychiatry: Journal for the Study of Interpersonal Processes* 26; 1: pp65–76.

Butler R (1995) 'The life review.' In: Haight B K and Webster J D (eds). *The Art and Science of Reminiscing.* London: Taylor and Francis, ppxvii–xxi.

Cocklin D (1990) In: Atkinson D and Williams F (eds). *Know Me As I Am. An anthology of prose, poetry and art by people with learning difficulties.* London: Hodder and Stoughton, p9.

Coleman P (1986) *Ageing and Reminiscence Processes.* Chichester: Wiley.

Cooper M (1998) 'Mabel Cooper's life story'. In: Atkinson D, Jackson M and Walmsley J (eds). *Forgotten Lives: Exploring the history of learning disability.* Kidderminister: Bild.

de Klerk-Rubin V (1994) 'How validation is misunderstood.' In: *Journal of Dementia Care* 2; 2: pp14–16.

de Klerk-Rubin V (1995) 'A safe and friendly place.' In: *Journal of Dementia Care* 3; 3: pp22–24.

Dobrof R (1984) 'Introduction: A time for re-claiming the past.' In: Kaminsky M (ed). *The Uses of Reminiscence: New ways of working with older adults.* London: Haworth, ppxvii–xviii.

Eurolink Age (1996) *Older People and New Technology.* First European Network Meeting Report and Directory (September 1995). London: Eurolink Age.

Feil N (1992) *Validation: The Feil Method.* Cleveland: Edward Feil Productions.

Foster N (1996) *Music and Alzheimer's Disease: Past, present and future.* Report of meeting at Royal Holloway College, London, 24 August 1996.

Fry P S (1995) 'A conceptual model of socialization and agentic trait factors that mediate the development of reminiscence styles and their health outcomes.' In: Haight B K and Webster J D (eds). *The Art and Science of Reminiscing.* London: Taylor and Francis, pp49–60.

Goldsmith M (1996) *Hearing the Voice of People with Dementia: Opportunities and obstacles.* London: Jessica Kingsley.

Haight B K (1998) 'Use of life review and life story books in families with Alzheimer's disease.' In: Schweitzer P (ed). *Reminiscence in Dementia Care.* London: Age Exchange, pp85–90.

Help the Aged Education Department (1981) *Recall.* London: Help the Aged.

Hunt L, Marshall M and Rowlings C (eds) (1997) *Past Trauma in Late Life.* London: Jessica Kingsley.

Kemp M (1978) *Audio-visual Reminiscence Aids for Elderly People Including the Mentally Frail.* London: DHSS.

Killick J (1994) 'There's so much more to hear when you stop and listen to individual voices.' *Journal of Dementia Care* 2; 5: pp16–17.

Killick J (1997) *You Are Words: Dementia poems.* London: Hawker.

Kitwood T (1997) *Dementia Reconsidered.* Buckingham: Open University Press.

Kurokawa Y (1996) 'Couple work with Japanese dementia patients.' In: *Reminiscence* 13: p18.

Langley D and Langley G (1983) *Dramatherapy and Psychiatry.* London: Croom Helm.

McConkey J (1997) *The Anatomy of Memory: An anthology.* Oxford: Oxford University Press.

Marshall M (1998) 'How it helps to see dementia as a disability.' In: *Journal of Dementia Care* 6; 1: pp15–17.

Mills M (1998) 'Using the narrative in dementia care.' In: Bornat J. *Biographical Interviews: The link between research and practice.* London: Open University/CPA.

Mistry T and Brown A (1991) 'Black/white co-working in groups.' In: *Groupwork* 4; 2: pp101–118.

Pear T (1922) *Remembering and Forgetting.* London: Methuen.

Powell A (1995) 'Depression and dementia.' In: *Journal of Dementia Care* 3; 4: pp28–29.

Read P (1996) *Returning to Nothing: The meaning of lost places.* Cambridge: Cambridge University Press.

Romaniuk J and Romaniuk M (1981) 'Looking back: an experimental analysis of reminiscence functions and triggers.' In: *Experimental Aging Research* 7: pp477–489.

Ruth J E (1996) Personal communication to the author.

Shulman L (1979) *The Skills of Helping Individuals and Groups.* Illinois: Itasca.

Sim R (1997) 'Portraits that tell a story.' *Journal of Dementia Care* 5; 16: pp6–7.

Sumpton J (1994) 'Environmentally friendly.' In: *Journal of Dementia Care* 2; 5: p9.

Tarman V (1988) 'Autobiography: The negotiation of a lifetime.' *International Journal of Aging and Human Development* 27; 3: pp171–191.

Thompson P (1988) *The Voice of the Past: Oral history*. Oxford: Oxford University Press.

Tuckman B W (1965) 'Developmental sequence in small groups.' In: *Psychological Bulletin* 63: pp384–399.

Warrington J (1996) *Depression and Dementia: Co-existence and differentiation*. Stirling: Dementia Services Development Centre.

Watt L M and Cappeliez P (1995) 'Reminiscence interventions for the treatment of depression in older adults'. In: Haight B K and Webster J D (eds). *The Art and Science of Reminiscing: Theory, research methods and applications*. London: Taylor and Francis.

Watt L and Wong P (1990) 'A taxonomy of reminiscence and therapeutic implications.' In: *Journal of Gerontological Social Work* 16: pp37–57.

Webster J D (1997) 'The reminiscence functions scale: a replication.' In: *International Journal of Aging and Human Development* 44; 2: pp137–149.

Wong P T and Watt L M (1991) 'What types of reminiscence are associated with successful ageing?' *Journal of Psychology and Ageing* 6; 2: pp272–279.

Woods B (1994) 'Reading around reality orientation.' In: *Journal of Dementia Care* 2; 2: pp24–25.

Yow V (1994) *Reconsidering Oral History: A practical guide for social scientists*. New York: Sage.

APPENDIX 1

Recording Sheets

This section gives examples of forms that you can use or adapt to keep a record of your reminiscence work. They can be easily modified to record work with individuals. These forms were developed by Michael Bender and I am grateful for permission to reproduce them.

Form 1 Personal History (pp 164–166) summarises background information on each individual. If possible much of this information should be obtained during an initial interview. It can be added to subsequently.

Form 2 Reminiscence Group – Individual Record (pp 167–168) summarises the response of each member at each session. Complete after each session by rating participants' responses on a 0–4 scale.

Form 3 Reminiscence Group – Group Record (pp 169–170) summarises the response of all members at each session and records attendance. Complete after each session by rating responses on a 0–4 scale.

Form 4 Reminiscence Group – Leader(s)' Record (pp 171–172) refers to the content and process of each session. It also includes notes on debriefing and supervision meetings. It is best completed jointly by the leaders as soon as possible after each session.

Form 5 Clearance Form (p 173) This is a consent form. It is important to have written consent from each participant if there is any likelihood that contributions may be used publicly.

1 Personal History

A personal history of

Information obtained from

History compiled by

Date

How person likes to be addressed

Date of birth

Family details

Person's name

Spouse's name

Maiden name

Date married

Date bereaved

Children

Spouses

Grandchildren

Mother's name

Father's name

Brothers and sisters

Close friends and relatives

Additional information

Place of origin

Length of time spent in area

First language

Places of special significance (and reason why)

Previous occupations

Achievements or interesting events in life

Hobbies and interests

Favourite pets

Religion

Church attended

Particular likes

Particular dislikes

Best method of communication

Right/left handed

Eyesight

Hearing

Special medical conditions (e.g. diabetes, allergies)

Additional information

2 Reminiscence Group – Individual Record

Group member's name

Activity

Sessions	1	2	3	4	5	6	7	8
Date								

Willingness to join group

0 Refused to join group

1 Needed persuading

2 Needed reminding

3 Came along without prompting

Memory

0 No recall

1 Recalled odd incidents

2 Good recall without prompting

3 Memory intact

Interaction (spontaneity)

0 Disruptive

1 Offered nothing at all

2 Spoke only if asked

3 Responded to other members

4 Spoke only when asked ☐ ☐ ☐ ☐ ☐ ☐ ☐ ☐

Participation/responsiveness (need not be verbal)

0 No response ☐ ☐ ☐ ☐ ☐ ☐ ☐ ☐

1 Little response/uncooperative ☐ ☐ ☐ ☐ ☐ ☐ ☐ ☐

2 Active participation when
prompted ☐ ☐ ☐ ☐ ☐ ☐ ☐ ☐

3 Active participation without
prompting ☐ ☐ ☐ ☐ ☐ ☐ ☐ ☐

Enjoyment

0 Showed no signs of enjoyment ☐ ☐ ☐ ☐ ☐ ☐ ☐ ☐

1 Occasionally showed pleasure ☐ ☐ ☐ ☐ ☐ ☐ ☐ ☐

2 Enjoyed majority of session ☐ ☐ ☐ ☐ ☐ ☐ ☐ ☐

3 Thoroughly enjoyed session ☐ ☐ ☐ ☐ ☐ ☐ ☐ ☐

Comments

3 Reminiscence Group – Group Record

Staff

Activity

Date

Members' names	Willingness to join group	Memory	Interaction	Participation	Enjoyment

Main topics discussed/material used

Themes

Comments

Suggestions

4 Reminiscence Group – Leader(s)' Record

Session no.

Date/time of session

Group leaders

Group members

Reasons for absences if any

Changes since last session

Intended outline of session

Theme

Topics covered

Group activity and process

Notes on the individuals

Interaction between group leaders

Overall assessment of session

Comments/suggestions

Debriefing after session

Supervision

5 Clearance Form

Your contribution of

```
┌─────────────────────────────────────────────────────────────┐
│                                                             │
└─────────────────────────────────────────────────────────────┘
```

will form part of the collection of material relating to the past and present. This form has been drawn up in order to ensure that we use your contribution only in accordance with your wishes.

1 May we use your contribution:

    a for public reference?   Yes/No

    b for research purposes?   Yes/No

    c for educational use (in seminars, workshops, schools, colleges, universities)?   Yes/No

    d for broadcasting purposes (radio or TV)?   Yes/No

    e as a source of information that may be published?   Yes/No

    f in a public performance, display or exhibition?   Yes/No

2 May we mention your name?   Yes/No

Are there any further restrictions you wish to place on this material? (please specify)

```
┌─────────────────────────────────────────────────────────────┐
│                                                             │
│                                                             │
│                                                             │
│                                                             │
└─────────────────────────────────────────────────────────────┘
```

Signature of interviewee   Date

```
┌───────────────────────────┐   ┌───────────────────────────┐
│                           │   │                           │
└───────────────────────────┘   └───────────────────────────┘
```

Signature of principal family carer   Date
(if appropriate)

```
┌───────────────────────────┐   ┌───────────────────────────┐
│                           │   │                           │
└───────────────────────────┘   └───────────────────────────┘
```

Signature of interviewer   Date

```
┌───────────────────────────┐   ┌───────────────────────────┐
│                           │   │                           │
└───────────────────────────┘   └───────────────────────────┘
```

Signature of professional carer   Date

```
┌───────────────────────────┐   ┌───────────────────────────┐
│                           │   │                           │
└───────────────────────────┘   └───────────────────────────┘
```

APPENDIX 2

Reminiscence and National Vocational Qualifications

Care Awards have been available since 1992, but the existing arrangements were replaced in April 1998. The new NVQs/SVQs have been accredited for five years (1998–2003) but the earlier awards remain valid and valued. If you are already registered with a scheme and you wish to have your reminiscence work assessed, you should clarify the position with your workplace assessor when preparing your work plan. If you are not already enrolled, seek guidance from your line manager or local scheme co-ordinator when seeking initial information about enrollment.

The new arrangements offer four improvements. They are intended to:

- provide user-friendly language and layout;
- provide flexible qualification structures;
- streamline the assessment system;
- cover identified gaps.

NVQs/SVQs Care Awards are available at different levels. The levels are related to the complexity of different jobs. Level 1 refers to the simplest job and Level 5 the most complex, senior job. Each level is divided into units and units are divided into elements. A specified number and type of units consisting of both mandatory and optional units is required at each level.

Candidates choose the level and the units that are most applicable to their job and best match its responsibilities. The work for and assessment of each unit is undertaken at a pace suited to each person's working situation. Each completed unit contributes to or accumulates towards the NVQ award and work submitted for one unit can be used, if relevant, towards the assessment of another unit. Neither levels nor units within levels need to be completed in any set order.

This approach is meant to build on what you already know, offer flexible training and a nationally recognised qualification. The training is closely linked to actual day-to-day work and its satisfactory performance in the workplace in health and social care services of all kinds.

NVQs/SVQs are designed to guarantee high quality services for patients, clients and carers. They do this by clearly specifying the knowledge, understanding, practical and thinking skills that underpin the work staff are required to do.

The NVQs/SVQs in Care at Levels 2 and 3 are meant for staff involved in directly providing care under the supervision of professionally qualified staff or designated line managers. The workplace can be either a statutory, voluntary or private facility and work may be undertaken in residential, hospital, day care, foster care and domiciliary care settings.

It may be possible to have reminiscence work credited for NVQs/SVQs in Care at Levels 2 and Level 3. As there is no explicit reference to reminiscence work in the official Care Consortium publications on Care Awards, it is not possible to say with certainty that this could be done, although it is highly likely that reminiscence work could be credited either as a unit or an element within a unit.

Care Level 2 requires four mandatory units, plus five optional units. These optional units are divided into two groups, A and B. At least three options must come from Group A. The units most relevant to reminiscence work are in Option Group B. They are: W8 'Enable individuals to maintain contacts in potentially isolating situations'; X1 'Contribute to the support of clients during development programmes and activities'; and Z13 'Enable clients to participate in recreation and leisure activities.' Reminiscence could possibly form an element in other units, for example CL1 (Mandatory), CL2 (Option Group A) or CL5 (Option Group B).

At Care Level 3, five mandatory units are required, plus seven optional units, at least four of which must come from Group A. The unit X16 (Option Group B) 'Prepare, implement and evaluate agreed therapeutic activities' is most obviously relevant to reminiscence work. It could also possibly be an element within many other units listed in the Mandatory, Option A and Option B groups.

NVQs/SVQs are different from traditional qualifications. They:

- have no entry barriers. Prior qualifications are not required;
- are open to anyone regardless of length of service, ethnic background, age or gender;
- require clarity about the role, responsibilities and contribution expected of staff;

- do not depend upon a single training course or one method of assessment;
- assess performance as well as knowledge, not by exams but by a portfolio;
- permit more flexibility, recognition and transfer of competence between jobs.

Assessment is undertaken in the workplace. Various methods for doing this are used. They include the workplace assessor observing actual work being done: by questioning; by statements from other people involved in the work; by simulations; and by case studies, assignments and projects. This varied approach leads not to pass or fail judgments, but to statements of competence, or not yet competent which give further opportunities for remedying deficiencies and achieving the required standards. A system of internal verifiers who 'sign off' the work once a unit has been completed helps ensure high quality national standards in training and assessment are maintained.

NVQs/SVQs are specially designed to make sure that staff acquire the skills required by employers, but they also permit great flexibility of training and its accreditation both within jobs and between different jobs and places of work.

APPENDIX 3

Resource Agencies

Age Concern Training
77 High Green
Cannock WS11 1BR
Tel: 01543 503660
Fax: 01543 504640

In-house training service and short courses at various locations throughout England. One-day reminiscence courses; advice and information; services for older people; campaigning and advocacy; publications.

Age Exchange Reminiscence Centre
11 Blackheath Village
Blackheath
London SE3 9LA
Tel: 0181-318 9105/3504
Fax: 0181-318 0060
E-mail: ageexchange@lewisham.gov.uk

Museum, shop, exhibitions, theatre, publisher of reminiscence books and materials, reminiscence sessions, boxes of artefacts for hire, inter-generational work, conferences and training workshops. Office of European Reminiscence Network and *Reminiscence Magazine.*

Age and Opportunity
Marino Institute
Griffith Avenue
Dublin 9
Ireland
Tel: +353 1 837 0570
Fax: +353 1 837 0591
E-mail: ageandop@indigo.ie

Publisher and distributor of *Ireland Recall.*

Alzheimer's Disease Society
Gordon House
10 Greencoat Place
London SW1P 1PH
Tel: 0171-306 0606

Service provision, carers' support groups, information, campaigning and publications.

British Library National Sound Archive
96 Euston Road
London NW1 2DB
Tel: 0171-412 7405
Fax: 0171-412 7441
E-mail: Rob.Perks@bl.uk

National Life Story collection, and free listening and viewing service.

Disabled Living Foundation
380–384 Harrow Road
London W9 2HU
Tel: 0870 603 9177

Information about aids to help you cope with a disability.

Eurolink Age New Technology Network
c/o Age Concern England
Astral House
1268 London Road
London SW16 4ER
Tel: 0181-679 8000
Fax: 0181-679 6727
E-mail: activage@ace.org.uk

A network of people running projects promoting opportunities for elders to develop computing skills for recreational, educational and developmental purposes.

European Reminiscence Network
See Age Exchange

Friends of the Elderly
25 Bolton Street
Dublin 1
Tel: +353 1 873 1855

Publisher and distributor of *Dublin Recall*.

Help the Aged
16–18 St James's Walk
London EC1R 0BE
Tel: 0171-253 0253

Publisher of *Recall* (now out of print but available through libraries and social agencies).

Hospital Arts
St Mary's Hospital
Hathersage Road
Manchester M13 OJH
Tel: 0161-256 4389

Uses arts and reminiscence to benefit people in health care situations.

Hulton Picture Company
21–31 Woodfield Road
London W9 2BA
Tel: 0171-266 2662

Picture library and provider of photographic prints.

International Society for Reminiscence and Life Review
c/o John Kunz
Mental Health Outreach Network
502 East Second Street
Duluth
Mn USA

A North American-based network of reminiscence practitioners and researchers.

Journal of Dementia Care
Hawker Publications
13 Park House
140 Battersea Park Road
London SW11 4NB
Tel: 0171-720 2108
Fax: 0171-498 3023

Published six times a year.

Kensington and Chelsea Community History Group
Methodist Church Centre
240B Lancaster Road
London W11 4AH
Tel: 0171-792 2282
Fax: 0171-792 4426

Memories groups, reminiscence training courses, inter-generational work in schools, projects, exhibitions, publications, training and supporting reminiscence volunteers with housebound elders.

Living Archive
Old Bath House
205 Stratford Road
Wolverton
Milton Keynes MK12 5RL
Tel: 01908 322568
E-mail: info:@lap.powernet.co.uk

Publications; arts project; local archive; reminiscence; older people's theatre group.

Living History Unit
Leicester City Council
Arts and Leisure Department
New Walk Centre
Welford Place
Leicester LE1 6ZG
Tel: 0116 252 7334

Network of people and organisations interested in Leicester's history; *Living History* newsletter; produces videos and publications; photographic and document archive.

Lothian Health Education Resource Centre
61 Grange Loan
Edinburgh EH9 2ER
Tel: 0131-447 6271

National Extension College
18 Brooklands Avenue
Cambridge CB2 2HN
Tel: 01223 316644

Publisher and distributor of open/distance learning materials.

Oral History Society
c/o Department of Sociology
University of Essex
Colchester CO4 3SQ
Tel: 0171-412 7405
Fax: 0171-412 7441
E-mail: Rob.Perks@bl.uk

Conferences, publications and specialist advice. Publishes *Oral History*.

Polkaville Community Cooperative
Storyville Archives Ltd
Suite 5
Whingate Business Park
Whingate
Leeds LS12 3BP
Tel: 0113 289 0087
E-mail: storyville@polkaville.com

Creators of *Comma*, a multi-media CD-ROM software programme for archiving personal and community photographs, film, video and other information with linked text.

Rafe Project (Reminiscence Approaches with the Frail Elderly)
Wensum Lodge
169 King Street
Norwich NR1 1QW
Tel: 01603 666330
Fax: 01603 767349

Reminiscence and craft activities for carers of older people, those with dementia and learning difficulties. Reminiscence training and development.

Reminiscence Database
37 Long Park
Modbury
Devon PL21 0RP

A flexible database available as printed copy or disk. Contains over 400 coded entries which are periodically updated.

Royal National Institute for the Blind
224 Great Portland Street
London W1N 6AA
Tel: 0171-388 1266

Information and advice, resources and publications.

Royal National Institute for Deaf People
105 Gower Street
London WC1E 6AH
Tel: 0171-387 8033

Information and advice, resources and publications.

Service and Practice Development Team (EMI)
Royal Hamadryad Hospital
Hamadryad Road
Cardiff CF1 6UQ
Tel: 01222 494952
Fax: 01222 496431

Library of reminiscence materials, *Signpost* journal and information for those working with and caring for people with dementia and elderly mentally ill people in South Glamorgan. Advice on reminiscence to others in Wales.

Sonas Apc
38 Belevedere Place
Dublin 1
Ireland
Tel and Fax: +353 1 836 6874

Activating potential for communication with frail older people including people with dementia. Training workshops in using a taped, structured, multi-sensory programme utilising touch, music, exercise and reminiscence.

Sound Sense
Riverside House
Rattlesden
Bury St Edmunds IP30 0SF
Tel: 01449 736287

Advice and information service on music and disability. Quarterly journal *Sounding Board* incorporating *Music News* previously published by the National Music and Disability Services.

Ulster Folk and Transport Museum
153 Bangor Road
Cultra
Holywood
County Down BT18 0EU
Tel: 01232 428428

Memorabilia, sound archive and photographic collection. BBC Northern Ireland sound archive.

WEA Scotland
Riddle's Court
322 Lawnmarket
Edinburgh EH1 2PG
Tel: 0131-226 3456
Fax: 0131-220 0306

Salt of the Earth project designed to create learning opportunities for disadvantaged adult groups through reminiscence, local history and personal history in urban and rural Scotland.

Winslow Press
Telford Road
Bicester
Oxon OX6 0BR
Tel: 01869 244644
Fax: 01869 320040
E-mail: winslow@dial.pipex.com

Publisher and distributor of reminiscence books and materials.

ABOUT AGE CONCERN

Reminiscence and Recall is one of a wide range of publications produced by Age Concern England, the National Council on Ageing. Age Concern cares about all older people and believes later life should be fulfilling and enjoyable. For too many this is impossible. As the leading charitable movement in the UK concerned with ageing and older people, Age Concern finds effective ways to change that situation.

Where possible, we enable older people to solve problems themselves, providing as much or as little support as they need. Our network of 1,400 local groups, supported by 250,000 volunteers, provides community-based services such as lunch clubs, day centres and home visiting.

Nationally, we take a lead role in campaigning, parliamentary work, policy analysis, research, specialist information and advice provision, and publishing. Innovative programmes promote healthier lifestyles and provide older people with opportunities to give the experience of a lifetime back to their communities.

Age Concern is dependent on donations, covenants and legacies.

Age Concern England

1268 London Road
London SW16 4ER
Tel: 0181-679 8000

Age Concern Cymru

4th Floor
1 Cathedral Road
Cardiff CF1 9SD
Tel: 01222 371566

Age Concern Scotland

113 Rose Street
Edinburgh EH2 3DT
Tel: 0131-220 3345

Age Concern Northern Ireland

3 Lower Crescent
Belfast BT7 1NR
Tel: 01232 245729

PUBLICATIONS FROM AGE CONCERN BOOKS

Care Professional Handbook Series
Caring for Ethnic Minority Elders: A guide
Yasmin Alibhai-Brown

Caring for Ethnic Minority Elders examines the delivery of care to older people from ethnic minority groups. Including specific sections on Afro-Caribbean, Asian, Chinese, Vietnamese, Jewish, Polish and Turkish communities, the text:

- highlights the impact of varying cultural traditions
- examines the design of individual care packages
- considers how elders receive care

Yasmin Alibhai-Brown uses extensive case study material throughout to illustrate case histories, and to highlight a range of key issues such as society's attitudes towards elders, religion and culture, and the allocation of resources.

Designed to help every care professional working with ethnic minority elders, and particularly those concerned with planning the delivery of services, this book provides valuable insights, and guidance for developing and maintaining the highest standards of care.

£14.99   0–86242–188–8

Promoting Mobility for People with Dementia: A problem-solving approach
Rosemary Oddy

People with dementia must be encouraged and enabled to move and given the opportunity to do so frequently, with or without help, if they are to remain mobile. This new book outlines commonsense approaches to ease this task and help to maintain optimum levels of mobility for people with dementia for as long as possible, without jeopardising the health and safety of those who care for them.

Throughout this book many of the problems associated with mobility are identified and suggestions made on how to ease or overcome them. Finding ways of communicating effectively in order to promote movement is central to the approach, as is the importance of planning ahead. Based on years of experience, this book contains a wealth of fresh and practical suggestions for physiotherapists, occupational therapists, nurses and carers.

£14.99 0–86242–242–6

Health and care

The Community Care Handbook: The reformed system explained

Barbara Meredith

Written by one of the country's leading experts, the second edition of this hugely successful handbook provides a comprehensive overview of the first two years of implementation of the community care reforms and examines how the system has evolved. Containing extensive background information on the origins of the new system, this edition describes some of the experiences of those working in the field.

£13.99 0–86242–171–3

Health Care in Residential Homes

Dr Anne Roberts

Written in a clear, accessible style, this book provides comprehensive information for managers and other staff on maintaining residents' health and dealing with their health problems. Topics covered in detail include:

- health promotion
- essential body maintenance
- common illnesses of later life
- caring for frailer residents
- what to do in an emergency
- understanding confusion, dementia and mental frailty
- residents and their medicines
- terminal illness and bereavement
- getting help from other agencies

This immensely readable book will be welcomed by care managers and care staff working with older people as a vital point of reference and guidance.

£14.95   0–86242–156–X

The Trained Nurse's Teaching Pack

Gill Early and Sarah Miller

The Trained Nurse's Teaching Pack is a training programme designed to help nurses educate care assistant staff in six vital nursing areas:

- stomas
- physical care of the dying
- psychological care of the dying
- communication
- pressure sores
- catheters

This user-friendly teaching pack will enable trained nurses to provide high quality group-led training and effectively guide and reinforce staff skills and development.

The pack contains 26 key point overhead transparencies.

£27.99   0–86242–213–2

CareFully: A handbook for home care assistants, 2nd Edition

Lesley Bell

Comprehensive and informative, this new edition of a highly acclaimed guide provides key advice for home care workers in promoting independence. Packed with practical guidance, detailed information on good practice and recent developments in home care provision, all chapters are related to S/NVQ Level 2 revised units in care. Topics covered in full include:

- basic skills of home care assistants
- the health of older people
- receiving home care – the user perspective
- the importance of core values

- providing a service for the new millennium
- taking care of yourself

Complete with case studies, checklists and a unique new section on user's perspectives, this is a book to enable all home care workers to face their jobs with confidence and enthusiasm.

£12.99   0–86242–285–X

Business Skills for Care Management: A guide to costing, contracting and negotiating

Penny Mares

Involvement in buying care services for users is now part of everyday practice for many care managers. This involves many frontline workers in 'business' activities that may be entirely new – for example, handling contracts, costing care packages, negotiating prices with providers and monitoring the quality of service.

This book provides the practical, administrative and financial skills that are needed by staff to get the best out of the community care system for their clients. Practical, accessible, and easy to read, it guides the reader through the key stages involved, always emphasising that the aim is to achieve the best quality service for users.

£11.99   0–86242–191–8

Carers Handbook Series

The Carer's Handbook: What to do and who to turn to

Marina Lewycka

At some point in their lives millions of people find themselves suddenly responsible for organising the care of an older person with a health crisis. All too often such carers have no idea what services are available or who can be approached for support. This book is designed to act as a first point of reference in just such an emergency, signposting readers to many more detailed, local sources of advice.

£6.99   0–86242–262–0

Caring for Someone who is Dying

Penny Mares

Confronting the knowledge that a loved one is going to die soon is always a moment of crisis. And the pain of the news can be compounded by the need to take responsibility for the care and support given in the last months and weeks. This book attempts to help readers cope with their emotions, identify the needs that the situation creates and make the practical arrangements necessary to ensure that passage through the period is as smooth as possible.

£6.99   0–86242–260–4

Caring for Someone with an Alcohol Problem

Mike Ward

When drinking becomes a problem, the consequences for the carer can be physically and emotionally exhausting. This book will help anyone who lives with or cares for a problem drinker, with particular emphasis on caring for an older problem drinker.

£6.99   0–86242–227–2

Finding and Paying for Residential and Nursing Home Care

Marina Lewycka

Acknowledging that an older person needs residential care often represents a major crisis for family and friends. Feelings of guilt and betrayal invariably compound the difficulties faced in identifying a suitable care home and sorting out the financial arrangements. This book provides a practical step-by-step guide to the decisions that have to be made and the help that is available.

£6.99   0–86242–261–2

Choices for the Carer of an Older Relative

Marina Lewycka

Being a carer may mean many different things – from living at a distance and keeping a check on things by telephone to taking on a full-time caring role. This book looks at the choices facing someone whose parent or other relative needs care. It helps readers look at their own circumstances and their own priorities and decide what is the best role for themselves – as well as the person being cared for.

£6.99   0–86242–263–9

Caring for Someone who has Dementia

Jane Brotchie

Caring for someone with dementia can be physically and emotionally exhausting, and it is often difficult to think about what can be done to make the situation easier. This book shows how to cope and seek further help as well as containing detailed information on the illness itself and what to expect in the future.

£6.99   0–86242–259–0

Caring for Someone who has had a Stroke

Philip Coyne and Penny Mares

Although 100,000 people in Britain will have a stroke this year, many people are still confused about what stroke actually means. This books is designed to help carers understand stroke and its immediate aftermath. It contains extensive information on hospital discharge, providing care, rehabilitation, and adjustment to life at home.

£6.99   0–86242–264–7

Caring for Someone at a Distance

Julie Spencer-Cingöz

With people now living longer, sooner or later, we are likely to find ourselves looking after a loved one or a friend – often at a distance. This book will help you to identify the needs and priorities that have to be addressed, offering guidance on the key decisions to be made, minimising risks, what to look for when you visit, how to get the most out of your visits, dealing with your relative's finances and keeping in touch.

£6.99   0–86242–228–0

Money Matters

Your Rights: A guide to money benefits for older people

Sally West

A highly acclaimed annual guide to the state benefits available to older people. Contains current information on Income Support, Housing Benefit and Retirement Pensions, among other matters, and provides advice on how to claim.

For further information, please telephone 0181-679 8000.

Your Taxes and Savings: A guide for older people

Sally West and the Money Management Council

This annual guide explains how the tax system affects older people over retirement age, including how to avoid paying more than necessary. The information about savings covers the wide range of investment opportunities now available.

For further information please telephone 0181-679 8000.

If you would like to order any of these titles, please write to the address below, enclosing a cheque or money order for the appropriate amount made payable to Age Concern England. Credit card orders may be made on 0181-679 8000.

Mail Order Unit
Age Concern England
1268 London Road
London SW16 4ER

INFORMATION LINE

Age Concern produces over 40 comprehensive factsheets designed to answer many of the questions older people – or those advising them – may have, on topics such as:

- finding and paying for residential and nursing home care
- money benefits
- finding help at home
- legal affairs
- making a Will
- help with heating
- raising income from your home
- transfer of assets

Age Concern offers a factsheet subscription service that presents all the factsheets in a folder, together with regular updates thoughout the year. The first year's subscription currently costs £50; an annual renewal thereafter is £25.

> To order your FREE factsheet list, phone 0800 00 99 66 (a free call) or write to:
>
> **Age Concern**
> FREEPOST (SWB 30375)
> Ashburton
> Devon TQ13 7ZZ

INDEX

accommodation, designing 112
action plans, developing 152–154
activity groups 30–31
'Age' 7
Age Exchange Reminiscence Centre,
    Blackheath 12, 155, 177
aggressive behaviour 17, 82, 113, 117
Aldridge, David 115
Alzheimer's disease 106
    see dementia, people with
anxiety 53
assessments, care home 24–25
Atkinson, Dorothy 147, 149, 150
audio recordings 86–87
auditory triggers 66–67
autobiographical writing 17, 80, 81,
    133
    see also life story books

Barr-On, Dan 98
Bartlett, Liz 102
bearing witness 98
Bender, Michael 139
bereaved people 128, 129
Birren, B A and Birren, J E 79, 81
black/white co-working 98–100
Bornat, Joanna 13, 26
boxes, memory 85
Butler, R 10, 13, 78

cameras, use of 47
Cappeliez, P see Watt, L and
    Cappeliez, P
cassettes/cassette recorders 47–48,
    65, 66, 86 87
'catastrophic reactions' 122–123
childhood topics and triggers 71
children see inter-generational
    reminiscence

clothing topics and triggers 70
Cocklin, Doreen 149
Coleman, P 131
colour, issues of 98–100
computers:
    software programmes 48
    for writing life stories 88–89
confidence, lack of 139
confidentiality, issues of 49–50, 84
confrontation 61
confusion 107, 119
    see dementia, people with
cooking as trigger 68
Cooper, Mabel 149
co-operation/co-working 32, 33, 35,
    37, 153
    see also black/white co-working
counselling 31, 131, 133
couple reminiscence 120
'Crabbit Old Woman, A' 6–7
creative writing groups 82
crying 60, 113, 119–120
cultural heritage 26

day centres 13, 17, 20, 62
    managers' responsibilities 32–33
deafness see hearing problems
death 133
    see also bereaved people
de-briefing 37
de Klerk-Rubin, V 124
dementia, people with 23, 42,
    105–109
    communicating with 109–112
    and depression 127, 129
    and reality orientation 123–124
    reminiscence in small groups
        113–116

and specific prompted
    reminiscence work 116–123
and validation therapy 123, 124
depressed people 127–132
    and reminiscence work 130,
    131–133
difficult behaviour 24, 82–83
discrimination, racial 92, 99
dislike of reminiscence 1–2, 15
Dobrof, R 13
drama 14, 64, 82
drawing, autobiographical 14, 64, 81

emotions 60, 113, 119–120
    at ending of meetings 62–63
    see also depressed people
employment topics and triggers 72
ethical considerations 90
ethnic minority elders 92, 102
    differences in responses 93–94
    and inter-generational
        reminiscence 98, 101–102
    language difficulties 99–100
    and loss of homeland 94–95, 97
    and past trauma 98
    and racism 92, 99
    religious festivals 96–97
    selection of triggers 96
Eurolink Age New Technology
    Network 88
European Reminiscence Network
    12, 85, 155, 177
    *Remembering Yesterday, Caring
        Today* 153–154
evaluation of groupwork 37

family carers 13, 17, 26, 75, 83
    training 153–154
family history 26, 79
family trees 64, 85
Feil, N 124
film projects, use of 47

food as trigger 68, 102
Foster, Nick 116
Fry, P S 28
furnishings 112

gardens 77, 112
Goldsmith, M (1996) 109
'Grass' 112
grieving 83
    see also bereaved people
groups/groupwork 16, 21–22, 30–32
    arranging escorts 43
    beginning phase of meetings
        53–58
    duration of meetings 43
    ending phase of meetings 62–63
    equipment 47–48
    frequency of meetings 41–42
    leadership and staffing 32–33, 35,
        37
    location of meetings 42–43, 61–62
    membership and invitations
        37–41
    middle phase of meetings 58–62
    parties 63
    for people with communication
        problems 137–139
    for people with dementia
        113–116
    phases and stages 33–34
    refreshments 48
    seating 43–44
    setting outcomes 35
    size of groups 38–39
    themes and topics 44–45
    use of triggers *see* triggers
guilt, feelings of 131

Haight, B K 79
hearing problems, people with 39,
    44, 137, 140–141

Help the Aged 11–12
history, family 25, 26, 27
history groups, local 12–13, 31
home life topics and triggers 69
hospitals 13, 16, 43, 61
  photographs 147
hostile behaviour *see* aggressive
  behaviour
housework topics and triggers 70
Hulton Picture Company 64–65
Hunt, L, Marshall, M and
  Rowlings, C: *Past Trauma in
  Late Life* 98, 129
hyperactive people 113

immigrants *see* ethnic minority
  elders
individual reminiscence work 16,
  75–77
  autobiographical writing 80–82
  and communication problems
    137–138
  with people with dementia
    116–123
  with depressed people 132
  and difficult behaviour 82–83
  ethical considerations 90
  life review 78–80
  making records 77, 84–90
  use of triggers 77
inter-generational reminiscence 17,
  101–102
  and bearing witness 98
Internet, the 48
interpreters 99–100
invitations, giving 37–41

Jewish people 97, 98

Kemp, M 11
key workers 39–40, 82
Killick, John: *You Are Words:
  Dementia Poems* 110–112

Kitwood, Tom: *Dementia
  Reconsidered* 106
Kurokawa, Yukiko 120

Langley, Dorothy 27
Langley, Gordon 11, 27
language barriers 99
leaders, group 35, 37
  see groups/groupwork
learning disabilities, people with
  145–146
  life story work 148–150
  and loss and grief 146–147
  trigger materials 147–148
leisure topics and triggers 72
Lewy body dementia 106
  see dementia, people with
libraries 46, 89, 153
life lines 85
life review 17, 23, 78–80
life stories/life story work 16
  and people with dementia
    118–120
  and people with learning
    disabilities 148–150
  publishing 50
  recording 84–88
  using computers 88–89
  see also autobiographical writing;
    life reviews
life story books 84
lifescapes 86
lip-reading 140, 141
loss, feelings of 59–60, 83, 127–128,
  129
  of people with learning
    disabilities 146–147

McConkey, James 28
managers 32–33
Marshall, Mary 112
  see also Hunt, L

membership of groups 37–41
memorabilia 133–134
memory 28
  loss 107, 108
memory boxes 85
Mills, M 129
mime 14, 82
Mistry, T and Brown, A 100
morale: and types of reminiscers
    131–132
multi-infarct dementia 106
  see dementia, people with
museums 46, 72, 153
music and singing 14, 82
  and people with dementia
      115–116
  and people with speech problems
      142–143
  as triggers 46, 66
'mutual aid' groups 30

names, use of 54
National Extension College 89
National Vocational Qualifications
    2–3, 155, 174–176
nature and nurture 3
networking 155
newspapers 46, 65
noisy people 82

obsessional recollection 83, 113
old age, views of 3–4
Open University 155
oral history 11, 12–13
  see life stories/life story work
ownership rights 50, 84

painful recollections 15, 27, 59–60,
    119–120
painting, autobiographical 14, 64, 81
Pear, T 14
Personal History Forms 41, 164–166

photographs 64–65, 84, 85, 86
  of hospital life 147
pictures as triggers 77
  see also photographs
poems:
  'Age' 7
  'A Crabbit Old Woman' 6–7
  'Grass' 112
  'You Are Words' 111
poetry/poetry groups 14, 82
possessions, cherished 77, 133–134
Powell, A 106
problem-solving, reminiscence as 97
projectors, use of 47, 65
property rights 50, 84
psychotherapeutic groups 31
publication of life stories 50

questions, asking 58

racial issues/racism 92, 98–100
radio 66, 67
reactions, 'catastrophic' 122–123
Read, Peter 94
reality orientation (RO) 123–124
Recall programmes 12, 65
'reciprocal' groups 30
record forms 49–50, 163–173
records, making 77, 84–88
  and confidentiality 49–50, 84
  and ethical considerations 90
  for people with learning
      disabilities 148–150
  see also autobiographical writing
refreshments 48
religious festivals 96–97
reminiscence/reminiscence work
    1–2, 5
  characteristics 13–16
  definitions 10–11
  functions 20–28
  general v. specific 16–17

history 11–13
and life review 78–80
skills needed 18
as therapy 15, 80
Reminiscence Functions Scale (RFS) 27–28
repetitiveness 83, 113
research, need for 154
residential care homes 11, 13, 16, 20, 21–22, 23, 31, 62
assessments and care plans 24–25
cherished possessions 133–134
and depression 129–130
ethnic minority elders 96–97
managers' responsibilities 32–33
routines and difficult behaviour 83, 122
resource materials, collecting 152
RO *see* reality orientation
Romaniuk, J and Romaniuk, M 10
routines: and difficult behaviour 83, 122
Ruth, Jan-Eric 81

sadness *see* depressed people, painful recollections
school topics and triggers 71
senior staff, responsibilities of 32–33, 116–117
Shulman, L 34
shy people 57, 58, 76
sight problems, people with 39, 44, 137, 141–142
silent people 58, 60–61
Sim, Roger 63
singing 66, 115, 116, 142–143
slides, use of 47, 65
smells as triggers 67–68
song sheets 66
sounds as triggers 66–67
speech problems, people with 39, 137, 142–143

spontaneous reminiscence 75–77
story boards 86
Sumpton, John 112

tactile triggers 67
tape recordings *see* cassettes
Tarman, V 78–79
tastes as triggers 67–68
tears 60, 113, 119–120
themes and triggers 69–72
therapy, reminiscence as 15, 80
Thompson, Paul 26
time lines 85
topics and triggers 69–72
training 153–154, 155–156
triggers 16–17, 45–46, 59, 64, 152–153
auditory 66–67
in beginning phases of meetings 57–58
and 'catastrophic reactions' 123
cherished possessions 61, 77, 133–134
and childhood topics 71
and clothing topics 70
commercial packages 46, 72, 152
for people with dementia 114–115, 121, 123
for ethnic minority elders 96
and home life topics 69
and housework topics 70
for people with learning disabilities 147–148
and leisure topics 72
and school days topics 71
tactile 67
tastes and smells 67–68
visual 64–66
and wartime topics 70
and work topics 72
Tuckman, B W 34

uncooperative behaviour 82–83, 122
University of Greenwich 155
University of Sussex 156
University of Ulster: 'New Tricks'
    project 88

validation therapy 123, 124
vascular dementia 106
    see dementia, people with
video films 47, 65
    historical 66
video recordings 88
visual problems *see* sight problems
visual triggers 64–66
volunteers, reminiscence 13, 17, 101

Warrington, J 127
wartime topics and triggers 70
Watt, L and Cappeliez, P 129
Watt, L and Wong, P 28, 83
Webster, J D 130
    'Reminiscence Functions Scale'
        27–28
Wong, P *see* Watt, L and Wong, P
Woods, Bob 124
work topics and triggers 72
writing *see* autobiographical writing

'You Are Words' 111
Yow, Valerie 90